BEOWULF
AND THE FINNESBURG FRAGMENT

BEOWULF
AND THE FINNESBURG FRAGMENT

A TRANSLATION INTO
MODERN ENGLISH PROSE
BY

JOHN R. CLARK HALL
M.A., PH.D.

NEW EDITION

COMPLETELY REVISED WITH NOTES
AND AN INTRODUCTION BY
C. L. WRENN
M.A.
*Rawlinson and Bosworth Professor of Anglo-Saxon
at the University of Oxford*

WITH PREFATORY REMARKS BY
J. R. R. TOLKIEN
*Merton Professor of English Language and
Literature, Oxford*

GEORGE ALLEN & UNWIN LTD
RUSKIN HOUSE · MUSEUM STREET

FIRST PUBLISHED IN 1911
REVISED EDITION 1940
REVISED EDITION 1950
FOURTH IMPRESSION 1954
FIFTH IMPRESSION 1958

PRINTED IN GREAT BRITAIN
BY BRADFORD AND DICKENS
LONDON, W.C.1

FOREWORD

THE translation has been again revised in the light of recent scholarship, and the opportunity has been taken to correct misprints. An entirely new Introduction has been provided, designed to give the reader or student a quick view of the essential prolegomena to *Beowulf* as a preliminary to first reading and a preparation for the study of fuller and more learned critical editions.

The Notes have been greatly enlarged, so as to include not only points in which the translation differs from that required by Klaeber's text, but also a number of matters of special interest or difficulty which might be hard to sort out from Klaeber's very full technical treatment.

It is hoped that the general reader will gain some idea of this great poem from the translation and the less technical parts of the brief and simple Introduction; and that the professed student of the poem may make a more comfortable and effective approach than could well be had in his earliest stages from larger works. It is recommended that the student should read through the translation several times to assimilate fully the subject-matter, and with the aid of the Introduction, something of its general literary quality. Then *Beowulf* should be worked through without much detailed study with the aid of the Notes, using the translation to save time by gaining an idea of the contents of a given passage before attempting to work over its syntax and grammar. Then, this having been done, the student should be in a position to approach the elaborate works of Klaeber or other editors with far more profit in this indirect way than from the somewhat daunting immediate contact.

From the point of view of the student, this book is to be regarded as a kind of introduction to an edition with full apparatus. But it is also hoped that some of the Notes may here and there suggest new or interesting points of view.

Professor Tolkien's *Prefatory Remarks,* which have enabled matters of metre and diction to be omitted from the Introduction, are here reproduced unchanged save for the correction of an occasional misprint: for they must remain as the most permanently valuable part of the book.

C. L. WRENN

Oxford,
  January, 1949

CONTENTS

PREFATORY REMARKS

ON PROSE TRANSLATION OF "BEOWULF"

I

ON TRANSLATION AND WORDS

No defence is usually offered for translating *Beowulf*. Yet the making, or at any rate the publishing, of a modern English rendering needs defence: especially the presentation of a translation into plain prose of what is in fact a poem, a work of skilled and close-wrought metre (to say no more). The process has its dangers. Too many people are willing to form, and even to print, opinions of this greatest of the surviving works of ancient English poetic art after reading only such a translation, or indeed after reading only a bare "argument," such as appears in the present book. On the strength of a nodding acquaintance of this sort (it may be supposed,) one famous critic informed his public that *Beowulf* was "only small beer." Yet if beer at all, it is a drink dark and bitter: a solemn funeral-ale with the taste of death. But this is an age of potted criticism and pre-digested literary opinion; and in the making of these cheap substitutes for food translations unfortunately are too often used.

To use a prose translation for this purpose is, none-theless, an abuse. *Beowulf* is not merely in verse, it is a great poem; and the plain fact that no attempt can be made to represent its metre, while little of its other specially poetic qualities can be caught in such a medium, should be enough to show that "Clark Hall," revised or unrevised, is not offered as a means of judging the original, or as a substitute for reading the poem itself. The proper purpose of a prose translation is to provide an aid to study.

If you are not concerned with poetry, but with other matters, such as references to heroic names now nearly faded into oblivion, or the mention of ancient customs and beliefs, you may find in this competent translation all that you require for comparison with other sources. Or nearly all—for the use of " Anglo-Saxon " evidence is never, of course, entirely safe without a knowledge of the language. No translation that aims at being readable in itself can, without elaborate annotation, proper to an edition of the original, indicate all the possibilities or hints afforded by the text. It is not possible, for instance, in translation always to represent a recurring word in the original by one given modern word. Yet the recurrence may be important.

Thus "stalwart" in 198, "broad" in 1621, "huge" in 1663, "mighty" in 2140 are renderings of the one word *eacen*; while the related *eacencræftig,* applied to the dragon's hoard, is in 2280 and 3051 rendered "mighty." These equivalents fit the contexts and the modern English sentences in which they stand, and are generally recognized as correct. But an enquirer into ancient beliefs, with the loss of *eacen* will lose the hint that in poetry this word preserved a special connotation. Originally it means not "large" but "enlarged," and in all instances may imply not merely size and strength, but an *addition* of power, beyond the natural, whether it is applied to the super-human thirtyfold strength possessed by Beowulf (in this Christian poem it is his special gift from God), or to the mysterious magical powers of the giant's sword and the dragon's hoard imposed by runes and curses. Even the *eacne eardas* (1621) where the monsters dwelt may have been regarded as possessing, while these lived, an added power beyond the natural peril. This is only a casual example of the kind of difficulty and interest revealed by the language of Old English verse (and of *Beowulf* in particular), to which no literary translation can be expected to provide a complete index. For many Old English poetical words there are (naturally) no precise modern equivalents of the same scope and tone: they come down to us bearing echoes of ancient days beyond the shadowy borders of Northern history. Yet the compactness of the original idiom, inevitably weakened even in prose by transference to our looser modern language, does not tolerate long explanatory phrases. For no study of the fragmentary Anglo-Saxon documents is translation a complete substitute.

But you may be engaged in the more laudable labour of trying actually to read the original poem. In that case the use of this translation need not be disdained. It need not become a "crib." For a good translation is a good companion of honest labour, while a "crib" is a (vain) substitute for the essential

work with grammar and glossary, by which alone
can be won genuine appreciation of a noble idiom
and a lofty art.

Old English (or Anglo-Saxon) is not a very difficult
language, though it is neglected by many of those
concerned with the long period of our history during
which it was spoken and written. But the idiom and
diction of Old English verse is not easy. Its manner
and conventions, and its metre, are unlike those of
modern English verse. Also it is preserved frag-
mentarily and by chance, and has only in recent
times been redeciphered and interpreted, without the
aid of any tradition or gloss: for in England, unlike
Iceland, the old Northern poetic tradition was at
length completely broken and buried. As a result
many words and phrases are met rarely or only once.
There are many words only found in *Beowulf*. An
example is *eoten* "giant" 112, etc. This word, we
may believe on other evidence, was well known,
though actually it is only recorded in its Anglo-Saxon
form in *Beowulf*, because this poem alone has survived of the oral and written matter dealing with
such legends. But the word rendered "retinue" in
924 is *hose*, and though philologists may with confidence define this as the dative of a feminine noun
hōs (the Anglo-Saxon equivalent of Old High German
and Gothic *hansa*), it is in fact found in this line
of *Beowulf* alone; and how far it was not only
"poetical," but already archaic and rare in the time
of the poet, we do not know. Yet we need to know, if
a translation strictly true in verbal effect is to be

devised. Such lexical niceties may not trouble many
students, but none can help finding that the learning
of new words that will seldom or never again be
useful is one of the (accidental) difficulties presented
by Old English verse. Another is presented by the
poetical devices, especially the descriptive compounds, which, if they are seldom in fact "unnatural,"
are generally foreign to our present literary and
linguistic habits. Their precise meaning and full
significance (for a contemporary) is not always easy
to define, and their translation is a problem for the
translator over which he often must hesitate. A simple
example is *sundwudu,* literally "flood-timber" or
"swimming-timber." This is "ship" in 208 (the
riddle's bare solution, and often the best available,
though quite an inadequate, rendering), and "wave-
borne timbers" in 1906 (an attempt to unfold, at the
risk of dissipating it, the briefly flashed picture).
Similar is *swan-rad,* rendered "swan's-road" in 200:
the bare solution "sea" would lose too much. On the
other hand, a full elucidation would take far too long.
Literally it means "swan-riding": that is, the region
which is to the swimming swan as the plain is to the
running horse or wain. Old English *rad* is as a rule
used for the act of riding or sailing, not as its modern
descendant "road," for a beaten track. More difficult
are such cases as *onband beadurune* in 502, used of
the sinister counsellor, Unferth, and rendered "gave
vent to secret thoughts of strife." Literally it means
"unbound a battle-rune (*or* battle-runes)." What
exactly is implied is not clear. The expression has an

antique air, as if it had descended from an older time to our poet: a suggestion lingers of the spells by which men of wizardry could stir up storms in a clear sky.

These compounds, especially when they are used not with but instead of such ordinary words as *scip* "ship," or *sæ* "sea" (already twelve hundred years ago the terms of daily life), give to Old English verse, while it is still unfamiliar, something of the air of a conundrum. So the early scholars of the seventeenth and eighteenth centuries thought: to them, even when they understood Ælfred or Ælfric well enough, "Saxon poetry" often seemed a tissue of riddles and hard words woven deliberately by lovers of enigma. This view is not, of course, just: it is a beginner's misapprehension. The riddle element is present, but Old English verse was not generally dark or difficult, and was not meant to be. Even among the actual verse-riddles extant in Anglo-Saxon, many are to be found of which the object is a cameo of recognizable description rather than a puzzle. The primary poetic object of the use of compounds was compression, the force of brevity, the packing of the pictorial and emotional colour tight within a slow sonorous metre made of short balanced word-groups. But familiarity with this manner does not come all at once. In the early stages—as some to whom this old verse now seems natural enough can doubtless well remember —one's nose is ground close to the text: both story and poetry may be hard to see for the words. The grinding process is good for the noses of scholars, of any age or degree; but the aid of a translation may be a welcome relief. As a general guide, not only in those hard places which remain the cruces of the expert, this translation can be recommended.

The older version of Dr. Clark Hall did good service; but it must be admitted that it was often a faulty guide in diction—not only as representing the original (which is difficult or impossible fully to achieve), but as offering an harmonious choice of modern English words. It did not often rival the once famous oddities of Earle's *Deeds of Beowulf,*[1] though the "ten timorous trothbreakers together" in 2846 (reminiscent of the "two tired toads that tried to trot to Tutbury"), and the "song of non-success" in 787 (for *sigeleasne sang*—"a song void of triumph") are of a similar vintage. But it fell too often into unnecessary colloquialisms, such as "lots of feuds" 2028 (now "many"), quite alien to the tone of the original in its own day. Too often notables, visitors and subalterns appeared instead of the more fitting, and indeed more literally accurate, counsellors, strangers, and young knights. The fire-dragon appeared as a reptile and a salamander (2689); the jewels of his hoard were called "bright artistic gems."

The revision has as far as possible emended these things. Though hampered naturally by the fact that it is a revision, not a translation afresh, it is now a

---

[1] Several are to be found on p. 25 of that book: notably the renowned "boss of horrors" for *fyrena hyrde* 750, here rendered "master of crimes"; and "genial saloon" for *winsele* 771, here rendered "wine-hall." The suggestion of Grand Guignol and less reputable "pubs" is wholly false to the original.

better guide in these respects. But no translation, whatever its objects—a student's companion (the main purpose of this book), or a verse-rendering that seeks to transplant what can be transplanted of the old poetry—should be used or followed slavishly, in detail or general principle, by those who have access to the original text. Perhaps the most important function of any translation used by a student is to provide not a model for imitation, but an exercise for correction. The publisher of a tranlation cannot often hedge, or show all the variations that have occurred to him; but the presentation of one solution should suggest other and (perhaps) better ones. The effort to translate, or to improve a translation, is valuable, not so much for the version it produces, as for the understanding of the original which it awakes. If writing in (one's own) books is ever proper or useful, the emendation or refinement of a translation used in close comparison with a well-studied text is a good case for the use of a careful pencil. The making of notes of this sort is at any rate more profitable than the process more popular (especially with those reading for examinations): the inter-linear glosses in the text itself, which as a rule only disfigure the page without aiding the diffident memory.

A warning against colloquialism and false modernity has already been given by implication above. Personally you may not like an archaic vocabulary, and word-order, artificially maintained as an elevated and literary language. You may prefer the brand new, the lively and the snappy. But whatever may

be the case with other poets of past ages (with
Homer, for instance) the author of *Beowulf* did not
share this preference. If you wish to translate, not
rewrite, *Beowulf,* your language must be literary and
traditional: not because it is now a long while since
the poem was made, or because it speaks of things
that have since become ancient; but because the
diction of *Beowulf* was poetical, archaic, artificial (if
you will), in the day that the poem was made. Many
words used by the ancient English poets had, even in
the eighth century, already passed out of colloquial
use for anything from a lifetime to hundreds of
years.[2] They were familiar to those who were taught
to use and hear the language of verse, as familiar as
thou or *thy* are to-day; but they were literary,
elevated, recognized as old (and esteemed on that
account). Some words had never, in the senses given
to them by the poets, been used in ordinary language
at all. This does not apply solely to poetic devices
such as *swan-rad*; it is true also of some simple and
much used words, such as *beorn* 211, etc., and *freca*
1563. Both meant "warrior," or in heroic poetry
"man." Or rather both were used for "warrior" by
poets, while *beorn* was still a form of the word
"bear," [3] and *freca* a name of the wolf,[4] and they were

---

[2] Those who have access to texts and editions will easily find many
examples. Nouns, such as *guma* "man," are the largest class, but other
words of other kind are also frequent, such as *ongeador* 1595
"together"; *gamol* 58, etc. "old"; *sin* 1236, etc. "his." In these four
cases the ancestors of the normal modern words *mann, togædere, ald,
his* were already the current words in the poet's day.

[3] O.E. *bera*; O.N. *biörn* "bear."

[4] Literally "greedy one"; O.N. *freki,* wolf.

still used in verse when the original senses were forgotten. To use *beorn* and *freca* became a sign that your language was "poetical," and these words survived, when much else of the ancient diction had perished, as the special property of the writers of alliterative verse in the Middle Ages. As *bern* and *freik* they survived indeed in Northern English (especially in Scotland) down to modern times; and yet never in their long history of use in this sense, over a thousand years, were they ever part of the colloquial speech.

This sort of thing—the building up of a poetic language out of words and forms archaic and dialectal or used in special senses—may be regretted or disliked. There is nonetheless a case for it: the development of a form of language familiar in meaning and yet freed from trivial associations, and filled with the memory of good and evil, is an achievement, and its possessors are richer than those who have no such tradition. It is an achievement possible to people of relatively small material wealth and power (such as the ancient English as compared with their descendants); but it is not necessarily to be despised on that account. But, whether you regret it or not, you will misrepresent the first and most salient characteristic of the style and flavour of the author, if in translating *Beowulf,* you deliberately eschew the traditional literary and poetic diction which we now possess in favour of the current and trivial. In any case a self-conscious, and often silly, laughter comes too easily to us to be tempted in this way. The things we are here dealing with are serious, moving, and full of "high sentence"—if we have the patience and solidity to endure them for a while. We are being at once wisely aware of our own frivolity and just to the solemn temper of the original, if we avoid *hitting* and *whacking* and prefer "striking" and "smiting"; *talk* and *chat* and prefer "speech" and "discourse"; *exquisite* and *artistic* and prefer the "cunning craft" and "skill" of ancient smiths; *visitors* (suggesting umbrellas, afternoon tea, and all too familiar faces) and prefer "guests" with a truer note of real hospitality, long and arduous travel, and strange voices bearing unfamiliar news; *well-bred, brilliant,* or *polite noblemen* (visions of snobbery columns in the press, and fat men on the Riviera) and prefer the "worthy brave and courteous men" of long ago.

But the opposite fault, once more common, should be equally avoided. Words should not be used merely because they are "old" or obsolete. The words chosen, however remote they may be from colloquial speech or ephemeral suggestions, must be words that remain in literary use, especially in the use of verse, among educated people. (To such *Beowulf* was addressed, into whatever hands it may since have fallen.) They must need no gloss. The fact that a word was still used by Chaucer, or by Shakespeare, or even later, gives it no claim, if it has in our time perished from literary use. Still less is translation of *Beowulf* a fitting occasion for the exhumation of dead words from Saxon or Norse graves. Antiquarian sentiment and philological knowingness are wholly out of place. To render *leode* "freemen, people" by *leeds* (favoured by William Morris) fails both to translate the Old English and to recall *leeds* to life. The words used by the Old English poets, however honoured by long use and weighted with the associations of old verse, were emphatically those which had survived, not those which might have survived, or in antiquarian sentiment ought to have survived.

Different, though related, is the etymological fallacy. A large number of words used in *Beowulf* have descended to our own day. But etymological descent is of all guides to a fit choice of words the most untrustworthy : *wann* is not "wan" but "dark" ; *mod* is not "mood" but "spirit" or "pride" ; *burg* is not a "borough" but a "strong place" ; an *ealdor* is not an "alderman" but a "prince." The vocabulary of Old English verse may have philological interests but it had no philological objects.[5]

The difficulties of translators are not, however, ended with the choice of a general style of diction. They have still to find word for word : to deal with

[5] It is a habit of many glossaries to Old English texts to record, in addition to a genuine translation, also that modern word which is (or is supposed to be) derived from the Old English word, and even to print this etymological intruder in special type so that it is impressed on the eye to the disadvantage of the correct rendering. The habit is pernicious. It may amuse the glossators, but it wastes space upon what is in the circumstances an irrelevance. It certainly does not assist the memory of students, who too often have to learn that the etymological gloss is worse than useless. Students should handle such glossaries with suspicion. The reading of *Beowulf* is an opportunity for learning the Old English language and mastering a form of poetic expression. Lessons in the later history of English were better reserved for other occasions.

the so-called "synonyms" of Old English verse and
with the compounds. Translation of the individual
simple words means, or should mean, more than just
indicating the general scope of their sense: for
instance, contenting oneself with "shield" alone to
render Old English *bord, lind, rand* and *scyld*. The
variation, the *sound* of different words, is a feature of
the style that should to some degree be represented,
even if the differences of original meaning are neglected by the poet or no longer remembered—events
which in early Old English poetry probably occurred
far less often than is sometimes supposed. But in
cases where Old English has built up a long list of
synonyms, or partial equivalents, to denote things
with which Northern heroic verse was specially concerned—such as the sea, and ships, and swords, and
especially men (warriors and sailors), it will sometimes be found impossible to match its richness of
variation even with the most indiscriminate collection
of words. For *man* in *Beowulf* there appear at least
ten virtual synonyms: *beorn, ceorl, freca, guma,
hæleð* and *hæle, leod, mann* and *manna, rinc, secg,*
and *wer*.[6] This list can be extended to at least
twenty-five items by the inclusion of words whose
sense remained in varying degrees more specific,
though in heroic verse they could as a rule replace
the simple *mann*: words implying noble birth such as
æðeling and *eorl*; meaning youths or young men,

[6] Not all of these are strictly synonymous. *Ceorl, mann, wer,* were
also current words with proper senses (freeman, human being, adult
male or husband).

such as *cniht, hyse, maga, mecg*; or denoting the
various companions, followers, and servants of lords
and kings, such as *gædeling, geneat, gesið, scealc,
ðegn*; or explicitly signifying "warrior," such as
cempa, oretta, wiga, wigend. With this list not even a
hotch-potch series such as *man, warrior, soldier,
mortal, brave, noble, boy, lad, bachelor, knight,
esquire, fighter, churl, hero, fellow, cove, wight,
champion, guy, individual, bloke,* will compete: not
even in length, certainly not in fitness. In such a case
(the most extreme) we have to be content with less
variation—the total effect is probably not much
changed: our ears, unaccustomed to this kind of
thing, may be as much impressed by less. There is,
however, no need to increase our poverty by avoiding
words of chivalry. In the matter of armour and
weapons we cannot avoid them, since our only terms
for such things, now vanished, have come down
through the Middle Ages, or have survived from
them.   There is no reason for avoiding *knights,
esquires, courts,* and *princes.* The men of these legends
were conceived as kings of chivalrous courts, and
members of societies of noble knights, real Round
Tables. If there be any danger of calling up inappro-
priate pictures of the Arthurian world, it is a less one
than the danger of too many warriors and chiefs
begetting the far more inept picture of Zulus or Red
Indians. The imagination of the author of *Beowulf*
moved upon the threshold of Christian chivalry, if
indeed it had not already passed within.

The translation of the compounds sets a different

problem, already glanced at above. A satisfactory solution will seldom be arrived at by translation of the elements separately and sticking them together again: for instance, by rendering the "kenning" or descriptive compound *gleo-beam* 2263, denoting the harp, as "glee-beam," or (avoiding the etymological fallacy) as "mirth-wood." Of *brimclifu* 222 an accurate and acceptable translation may be "sea-cliffs," but this is a rare good fortune. A literal rendering of 81–5 *sele hlifade heah ond horngeaþ; heaðowylma bad laðan liges; ne wæs hit lenge ða gen ðæt se ecghete aðumsweoran æfter wælniðe wæcnan scolde* would be like this: "hall towered high and *horn-spacious; war-surges* awaited of hostile flame; it was not at hand yet that the *blade-hate* of *son-father-in-law* after *slaughter-malice* should awake." But this is certainly not modern English, even if it is intelligible.

It is plain that the translator dealing with these compounded words must hesitate between simply naming the thing denoted (so "harp" 1065, for *gomen-wudu* "play-wood"), and resolving the combination into a phrase. The former method retains the compactness of the original but loses its colour; the latter retains the colour, but even if it does not falsify or exaggerate it, it loosens and weakens the texture. Choice between the evils will vary with occasions. One may differ in detail from the present translation, but hardly (if one respects modern as well as ancient English) in general principle: a preference for resolution.

The compounds found in Old English verse are not, however, all of the same kind, and resolution is not in all cases equally desirable. Some are quite prosaic: made for the expression of ideas without poetic intention. Such words are found both in verse and prose, and their translation depends simply on their meaning as a whole. It is not necessary to "resolve" *mundbora*,[7] since the simple words "protector" or "patron" get as near as we can to the meaning of this word.

A larger, intermediate, class is formed by those words in which composition is used as a natural and living device of the contemporary English language. The distinction between verse and prose or colloquial use here lies mainly in the fact that these compounds are more frequent in verse, and coined with greater freedom. In themselves—even those which are only used, or at least are only recorded, in verse—they would sound as natural in contemporary ears as would *tobacco-stall* or *tea-drinker* in ours. Of this class are *heals-beag* "neck-ring," *bat-weard* "boat-guard," and *hord-wela* "hoard(ed) wealth"—three examples which (probably by mere chance) only occur in *Beowulf*. No "Anglo-Saxon" who heard or read them would have been conscious that they were combinations never before used, even if he had in fact never met them before. Our language has not lost, though it has much limited, the compounding habit. Neither "neck-ring" not "boat-guard" are recorded in the

[7] The "bearer of *mund*," that is, one who has taken an inferior or friendless man under his *mund* or "tutela."

Oxford Dictionary,[8] but they are inoffensive, although "hoard-wealth" is now unnatural. This class of compound is in general the one for which compound equivalents in modern English can with discretion most often be found or made.

But it shades off, as the intention becomes more fanciful or pictorial, and the object less to denote and more to describe or recall the vision of things, into the "poetic class": the principal means by which colour was given to Old English verse. In this class, sometimes called by the Icelandic name "kenning" (description), the compound offers a partial and often imaginative or fanciful description of a thing, and the poets may use it instead of the normal "name." In these cases, even where the "kenning" is far from fresh and has become the common property of verse-makers, the substitution of the mere name in translation is obviously as a rule unjust. For the kenning flashes a picture before us, often the more clear and bright for its brevity, instead of unrolling it in a simile.

I have called this the poetic class, because there is a poetic intention in their making. But compounds of this kind are not confined to verse: not even those which are poetic and fanciful. We find "kennings" in ordinary language, though they have then as a rule become trite in the process of becoming familiar. They may be no longer analysed, even when their form has not actually become obscured by wear. We

---

[8] *Boat-ward,* in the northern form *batward,* is recorded from Wyntoun's Chronicle of the fifteenth century—probably made afresh and not descended from Old English.

need not be led astray in our valuation of the living
compounds of poetry by such current "kennings" as
the prose *lichama* = body, or *hlafweard* = master. It
is true that *lichama* the "raiment of flesh," discardable,
distinct from the *sawol* or "soul" to which it was
intricately fitted, became an ordinary word for
"body," and in its later form *licuma* revealed the
evaporation of feeling for its analysis and full meaning.   It is true that *hlaf-weard* "bread-keeper" is
seldom found in this clear form, and usually appeared
as *hlaford* (whence our wholly obscured *lord*), having
become among the English the ordinary word for
" lord" or "master," often with no reference to the
bounty of the patriarch. But this emptying of significance is not true even of the most hackneyed of the
"kennings" of the poets. It is not true of *swanrad* 200,
beadoleoma 1523, *woruldcandel* 1965, *goldwine*
1171, *banhus* 2508, and the host of similar devices in
Old English verse.[9] If not fresh, in the sense of being
struck out then and there where we first meet them,
they are fresh and alive in preserving a significance
and feeling as full, or nearly as full, as when they
were first devised. Though *lic-hama* had faded into
licuma, though there is now "nothing new under the
sun," we need not think that *ban-hus* meant merely
"body," or such a stock phrase as *hæleð under
heofenum* 52 merely "men."

---

[9] On *swanrad,* see above. *Beado-leoma* "ray of light in battle" is a
sword (drawn and glinting) ; *woruld-candel* "candle of the world" is
the sun ; *goldwine* "goldfriend," is a lord or king (generous in gifts of
treasure to his kin and loyal knights); *ban-hus* "the house whose
timbers are bones" is the body.

He who in those days said and who heard
flæschama "flesh-raiment," *ban-hus* "bone-house,"
hreðer-loca "heart-prison," thought of the soul shut
in the body, as the frail body itself is trammelled in
armour, or as a bird in a narrow cage, or steam pent
in a cauldron. There it seethed and struggled in the
wylmas, the boiling surges beloved of the old poets,
until its passion was released and it fled away on
ellor-sið, a journey to other places "which none can
report with truth, not lords in their halls nor mighty
men beneath the sky" (50–52). The poet who spoke
these words saw in his thought the brave men of old
walking under the vault of heaven upon the island
earth [10] beleaguered by the Shoreless Seas [11] and the
outer darkness, enduring with stern courage the brief
days of life,[12] until the hour of fate [13] when all things
should perish, *leoht and lif samod.* But he did not say
all this fully or explicitly. And therein lies the
unrecapturable magic of ancient English verse for
those who have ears to hear: profound feeling, and
poignant vision, filled with the beauty and mortality
of the world, are aroused by brief phrases, light
touches, short words resounding like harp-strings
sharply plucked.

[10] *middangeard.*
[11] *garsecg.*
[12] *læne lif* 2845.
[13] *metodsceaft* 1180, 2815.

II

ON METRE

THESE prefatory remarks have so far been addressed primarily to students of Old English; but many things have been touched on that they will know already, and will find better elsewhere (especially in the original poem itself). For other readers have not been forgotten: those who may be obliged or content to take this translation as a substitute for the original. Such readers may find the remarks of interest: an aid in estimating what they miss, and in what ways Old English poetry differs from any modern rendering.

The remarks have been limited to verbal detail, and nothing has been said about the matter of the poem. For we are here dealing with *translation*. Criticism of the content could not be treated, even with inadequate brevity, in a preface twice as long.[1] There remains, however, one subject of major importance in considering any translation of a poem: the *metre*. A brief account of this is, therefore, here given. To students of Old English fuller and more accurate accounts are available. But they may find this sketch of use, although its object is to convey a notion of the metre (and the relation of this to style and diction)

[1] Reference must be made to the editions and other items in the short bibliography, p. 181. To these may be added Professor R. W. Chambers' essay, *"Beowulf" and the Heroic Age*, prefaced to Strong's metrical translation (1925), reprinted in *Man's Unconquerable Mind* (1939).

even to those who have little knowledge of the original language. The account is based on modern English, a novel but defensible procedure; for it brings out the ancestral kinship of the two languages, as well as the differences between them, and illustrates the old unfamiliar forms by words of whose tones and accents the student has living knowledge.

METRE

The Old English line was composed of two opposed word-groups or "halves." Each half was an example, or variation, of one of six basic patterns.

The patterns were made of *strong* and *weak* elements, which may be called "lifts" and "dips." The standard lift was a *long stressed* syllable (usually with a relatively high tone). The standard dip was an *unstressed* syllable, long or short, with a low tone.

The following are examples in modern English of normal forms of the six patterns:

A	falling-falling	:	*knights in	ármour.*
B	rising-rising	:	*the róar|ing séa.*
C	clashing	:	*on hígh	móuntains.*
D	{ *a* falling by stages	:	*bríght	árchàngels.*
	{ *b* broken fall	:	*bóld	brázenfàced.*
E	fall and rise	:	*híghcrèsted	hélms.*

A, B, C have equal feet, each containing a lift and dip. D and E have unequal feet: one consists of a single lift, the other has a subordinate stress (marked ′ ‵) inserted.

These are the normal patterns of four elements into which Old English words naturally fell, and into which modern English words still fall. They can be found in any passage of prose, ancient or modern. Verse of this kind differs from prose, *not* in re-arranging words to fit a special rhythm, repeated or varied in successive lines, but in choosing the simpler and more compact word-patterns and clearing away extraneous matter, so that these patterns stand opposed to one another.

The selected patterns were all of approximately equal metrical *weight* [2]: the effect of loudness (combined with length and voice-pitch), as judged by the ear in conjunction with emotional and logical *significance*.[3] The line was thus essentially a *balance* of two equivalent blocks. These blocks might be, and usually were, of different pattern and rhythm. There was in consequence no common tune or rhythm shared by lines in virtue of being "in the same metre." The ear should not listen for any such thing, but should attend to the shape and balance of the halves. Thus *the róaring séa rólling lándward* is not metrical because it contains an "iambic" or a "trochaic" rhythm, but because it is a balance $B + A$.

[2] To a full *lift* a value 4 may be given. The *subordinate stresses* (reduced in force and lowered in tone) that appear in such compounds as *highcrèsted* may be given value 2. But reduction also occurs in other cases. For instance, the second of two clashing stresses in a sentence; or of two juxtaposed words (of equal significance when separate), such as nouns and adjectives, tends to be reduced to approximate value 3. Using these rough values we see that the normal total value of each pattern is 10; C tends to be slightly lighter, and E to be slightly heavier.

[3] And so not purely phonetic, nor exactly measurable in figures (such as those used above) or by a machine.

Here is a free version of *Beowulf* 210–228 in this metre. The passage should be read slowly, but naturally: that is with the stresses and tones required solely by the sense. The lifts and dips utilized in this metre are those occurring in any given sequence of words in natural (if formal) speech, irrespective of whether the passage is regarded as verse or prose. The lines must not be strained to fit any familiar modern verse-rhythm. The reduced stresses (when their fall in force and tone approximates to value 2) are marked (`).

Beowulf and his Companions set sail

E	210	Tíme pàssed a|wáy. On the tíde | flóated	C
B		under bánk | their bóat. In her bóws | móunted	C
A +		bráve mèn | blíthely. Bréakers | túrning	A
A		spúrned the | shíngle. Spléndid | ármour	A
B		they bóre | abóard, in her bŏsom | píling	C
A	215	wéll-fòrged | wĕapons, then awáy | thrúst her	C
C		to vóyage | gládly văliant|-tìmbered.	A
A		She] wènt then over | wáve-tòps, wínd pur|súed her,	A
Da		fléet|, fóam-thròated like a flý|ing bírd ;	B
B		and her cúrv|ing prów on its cóurse | wáded,	C
C	220	till in dúe | seáson on the dáy | áfter	C
C		those séa|fàrers sáw be|fóre them	A
A +		shóre-clìffs | shímmering and shéer | móuntains,	C
E +		wíde cápes by the | wáves : to wát|er's énd	B
C		the shĭp had | jóurneyed. Then ashóre | swíftly	C
B	225	they léaped | to lánd, lórds of | Góthland,	A
E +		bóund fást their | bóat. Their býrn|ies răttled,	B
Db +		grím | géar of wár. Gód | thánked they thèn	Db
C		that their séa|-pằssage sáfe had | próven.	A

VARIATIONS

There were many variations on the basic patterns, some of which appear above. The principal were these.

1. *The dips*. The standard form was monosyllabic. There was, however, no *metrical* limit to the number of syllables in a dip, as long as they were genuinely *weak* (altogether inferior to the neighbouring stresses). This imposes a practical limit, as more than three really weak syllables are seldom found consecutively. Polysyllabic dips are frequent at the beginning of B and C.

> A, C, D end always in a monosyllabic dip in Old English, because words of the form $\acute{-} \times \times$ (like *hándily*, *ínstantly*) did not exist in the language. See p. xxxvii.

2. *The lifts*. A subordinate or reduced stress could act as a lift in A, B, C. So *váliant-tìmbered* 216, *séa-fàrers* 221, *séa-pàssage* 228.

3. *Breaking*. A lift could be "broken" into two syllables ´ ×, a *short stressed* followed by a *weak* syllable. That is *vĕssel, mĕllow*, are metrical equivalents of *boat, ripe*. Examples are seen above: A 216, 222; B 226; C 214, 224.

Examples of Da would be *bright păradises, hĕaven's archangels;* of Db *săllow pastyfaced;* of E *fĕatherwingëd shafts*. Both lifts could be broken: as *sĕven sălamanders* (Da) or *fĕatherwingëd ărrows* (E).

4. *Lightening*. The clash of long-stressed syllables, in a compound or in a sentence, could be relieved by

substituting a *single short stressed* syllable for the
second lift: for example, *gold-dĭggers* instead of *gold-
miners*. This is frequent in the clashing pattern C;
sea-păssage 228 is an example.

This can also occur in the subordinate stresses of
D*a* and E. Examples would be *wide grassmĕadows*
and *ill-wrĭtten verse*.

5. *Overweighting* and *Extension* (marked +).
These are a means of including certain common but
slightly excessive patterns in the metre; also of
adding weight to the line where required, and of
packing much significant word-material into a small
space.

Overweighting is most frequently seen in pattern
A. It consists in replacing the dip by a long (subordinate) stress. This may affect either or both of the
dips. Examples are seen in 212, 217, 222. An example
with double overweight would be *wéllmàde wárgeàr*.
The overweight or "heavy dip" may be broken: thus
wellfăshioned wargear or *wellmade wartrăppings*.

> Lightly stressed words (such as familiar and more or less
> colourless finite verbs and adverbs) often appear as
> "heavy dips." They are frequent in the first dips of B and
> C: as, B *càme wálk|ing hóme*; C *sàw stránge| vísions*. But
> these are not felt to be overweighted. The second dip of
> B, C and the dip of D, E may not be overweighted.

Overweighting of D and E takes the form of substituting a separate word for the subordinate stress.
The half-line then contains three separate words, and
the effect is heavier than the norm, unless one of these
words is of a naturally weak class. An example of

D*b* + is seen in 227, of E + in 223, 226.[4] An example of D*a* + would be *bright bládes dráwing*.

Extension is seen in the addition of a dip to the monosyllabic foot of D*a*, and occasionally of D*b*: thus *árdent árchàngels*; *bóld* and *brázenfàced*. A similar extension of E (as *highcrèsted hélmets*) is avoided.

The + patterns produced by overweighting and extension are excessive. They are usually confined to the first half of the line, and are regularly provided with *double* alliteration (see below). If the overweight in one foot is relieved by lightening in the other foot, then the total pattern is not excessive. Thus *wéllfòrged wĕapons* 215 is an example of a frequent variety of A, with "lightening" of the second lift after the long (subordinate) stress-*forged*. In *wènt then over wáve-tòps* 217 the overweight in *wave-tops* is compensated by the use of a lightly stressed unemphatic word as first lift. This special variety of A, with light beginning and heavy ending, is very frequently employed in lines marking (as here) a transition, or a new point in a narrative.

Syllables that did not fall inside a pattern were avoided—one of the reasons for the frequent asyndeton, and the love of short parallel sentences that mark the style. In good verse, such as *Beowulf*, the avoidance was strict in the second half-line, where such a sequence as *the rólling ócean* (dip + A, or B + dip) is practically never found. At the beginning of the line a prefixed dip, or "anacrusis," is

---

[4] But E in 210, and D*b* in 227 are not regarded as overweighted, since *pàssed, thèn* are not strong words.

occasionally used, chiefly in pattern A. An example occurs in 217 where *she*] is prefixed—the original has a similar anacrusis at the same point (see below).

ALLITERATION

Old English verse is called "alliterative." This is a misnomer in two ways. Alliteration, though important, is not fundamental. Verse built on the plan described above, if written "blank," would retain a similar metrical character. The so-called "alliteration" depends not on *letters* but on *sounds*. "Alliteration" or head-rhyme is, in comparison with end-rhyme, too brief, and too variable in its incidence, to allow mere letter-agreements or " eye-alliterations."

Alliteration in this metre is the agreement of the *stressed elements* in beginning with the *same consonant*,[5] or in beginning with *no* consonant.[5] All words beginning with a *stressed* vowel of any quality "alliterate," as *old* with *eager*. The alliteration of dips is not observed or of metrical importance. The alliteration of subordinate stresses (in A +, D, E) was avoided.

Arrangement

This was governed by the following rules:

1. One full lift in each half-line must alliterate. The key-alliteration or "head-stave" was borne by

---

[5] Phonetically speaking: thus *ph* will alliterate with *f*, but *sh* will not alliterate with *s*; *yes* will alliterate with *use*. In Old English, *st, sp, sc* are regarded as "consonantal dipthongs," each having an individual character. Each can only alliterate with itself, as *stone* with *stiff*, or *strong*. In other cases only the first of a group of initial consonants is compulsorily repeated.

the *first lift* in the *second* half. Thus *tide* 210 shows the head-stave to be *t*. With this the strongest lift in the first half must agree: thus *time*.

2. In the second half the *first lift only* can alliterate; the second lift must *not* alliterate.

3. In the first half both the lifts may alliterate. The stronger lift *must* bear the alliteration, the weaker can agree or not; but double alliteration was necessary in certain cases (see below).

A consequence of these rules is that the second half of the line must be so arranged that the stronger lift comes first. As a result the lines tend to end with the naturally inferior words (such as finite verbs), and so to fall away in *force* and *significance* together. There is normally an immediate rise of intensity at the beginning of the line, except in the case of light beginnings such as 217 (see above).

In all patterns the first lift is as a rule (for phonetic and syntactic reasons) the stronger. This is always the case in C, D*a* and *b*, and E. These patterns must bear the stave on the first lift or both (not only on the second lift).

> Dominance of the first lift distinguishes D*a* and D*b* from C and B respectively. Thus *sàw stránge vísions* is not D*a* but C with heavy first dip; *gàzed stónyfàced* is not D*b* but B with heavy first dip. Where, none the less, double alliteration occurs, as in *rùshed rédhànded* or *stàred stónyfàced*, we have intermediate patterns CD*a* and BD*b* respectively.

In pattern A dominance of the first lift was usual, but not compulsory. Not infrequently occur varieties with the second lift stronger. In these cases the second

lift must alliterate, and the first need not. Thus in
217 *pàssed* could be substituted for *wènt*.

Function

The main *metrical* function of alliteration is to *link*
the two separate and balanced patterns together into
a complete line. For this reason it is placed as near
the beginning of the second half as possible, and is
never repeated on the last lift (rule 2 above). Delay
would obscure this main linking function; repetition
by separating off the last word-group and making it
self-sufficient would have a similar effect.[6]

A subsidiary function is the quickening and relief
of heavy, overweighted or extended, patterns. These
(described above) all required *double alliteration*.
Examples are seen above in 212, 222, 226, 227.
Double alliteration is also frequent when both lifts
approach equality as in *under bánk their bóat* 211. It
is thus usually found when two strong words are co-
ordinated (and joined with *and, or*): as *boats and
barges; ferrets or foxes.*

Crossed alliteration is occasionally found in the
forms *ab|ab* and *ab|ba*. But this is either accidental,
or a gratuitous ornament, and not strictly metrical.
The alliteration must still be regular according to the
above rules, and the head-stave be borne by the first
lift of the second half. An example of *s, f|s, f* occurs
above in 221, and of *s, p|s, p* in 228.

Rhyme is employed in this verse only gratuitously,

---

[6] This can be plainly observed in the decadent alliterative verse of
Middle English where this rule is often broken.

and for special effects. It may appear in the normal form or as "consonantal rhyme," e.g. *und|and*. Both are found together in the original poem 212–13 *wundon||sund wið sande* where the special effect (breakers are beating on the shore) may be regarded as deliberate.

For further illustration the original of lines 210–228 is here given with metrical indications.

Db + 210		fýrst fórð gewát.	flóta wæs on ýðum	A
A		bát under béorge	béornas géarwe	A
C		on stéfn stígon.	stréamas wúndon	A
A		súnd wið sánde.	sécgas bǽron	A
C		on béarm nácan	béorhte frǽtwe	A
A+	215	gúð-sěaro gěatolíc.	gúman út scúfon	Da
A+		wěras on wíl-síð	wŭdu búndènne.	Da
A		ge]wát ðā ofer wǽg-hòlm	winde gefýsed	A
Db		flóta fǽmig-hèals	fúgle gelícost,	A
A		òððæt ymb án-tíd	óðres dógres [7]	A
A	220	wúnden-stèfna	gewǎden hǽfde,	C
C		ðæt ðā lïðènde	lánd gesáwon	A
A+		brím-clífu blícan,	béorgas stěape,	A
Da+		síde sǽ-næssas.	ðā wæs súnd-lïdan [8]	C
		éoletes [9] æt énde.	ðànon úp hráðe	C
A	225	Wědera lěode	on wáng stígon,	C
A+		sǽ-wŭdu sǽldon.	sýrcan hrýsedon	A
A		gúð-gewǽdo.	gŏde ðáncèdon	Da
C		ðæsðe him ýð-làde	ěaðe wúrdon.	A

The absence of B from this extract, and the predominance of A, are notable in comparison with the modern version.

[7] MS. *dōgores* a late form.

[8] MS. *sund liden,* emended by Crawford.

[9] Unknown or corrupt word, the metrical value of which is not determinable.

Owing (among other things) to inflexions, words of the A-type, as *làndes,* were very frequent in Old English. These have usually been replaced by monosyllables, as *land's,* or the B-phrase *of land.* The placing of a subordinate stress on the middle syllable of all trisyllables beginning with a long stress as *búndènne, ðáncèdon, líðènde* (compared with modern *hándily, ínstantly*) is another marked difference between the language of the Beowulf period and that of the present.

A literal rendering of this passage, word by word and in the same order, would run as follows. Words expressed in Old English by inflexions are in brackets.

210 ‖Time on departed.   B̲ was on Ws
        B under hill.   M̲ eager
        on prow strode.   Ws rolled
        S against sand.   M̲ bore
        into bosom (of) B̲   bright trappings
215   war-gear wellmade.   M̲ out thrust
        M̲ on wish-journey   timber fastened.‖
        Departed men over W-S   (by) wind urged
        B̲ foamy-neck   (to) bird likest,
        until after due-time   (of) second day
220   curved-prow [= B]   advanced had,
        that those voyagers   land saw
        S-cliffs gleaming,   hills steep,
        long S-capes.   then it was (for) S-voyager [= B]
        (of) ? waterway at end.   thence up quickly
225   (of) Wederas M̲   on plain strode,
        S-timber [= B] roped——shirts rattled
        war-raiment——God thanked
        that (for) them W-passage   easy proved.‖

The poetical words are underlined. In addition, the compounds *war-gear* 215, *wish-journey* 216, *foamy-neck* 218, *curved-prow* 220, *sea-cliffs* 222, *sea-capes* 223, *sea-timber* 226, *war-raiment* 227, *wave-*

passage 228, are poetical, whether the separate elements are so or not.

Here B represents three words for *boat,* two poetical (*flota, naca*) and one normal (*bāt*); in addition there are the "kennings" in 220, 223, 226. W represents three words for *wave,* one normal (*wǣg*), one more literary and archaic but not confined to verse (*ȳð*), and one (*strēam* "current, stream") whose application to the sea is mainly poetical. M represents five words for *men,* different in each case, three poetical (*beornas, secgas, guman*), and two used in prose (*weras* "adult males, husbands"; *lēode* "people"). S represents four words for *sea,* three poetical (*sund,* in prose "swimming"; *holm, brim*), and one normal (*sǣ*).

The letters B, W, M, S are here used simply to show the frequency of the poetical "synonyms," and the way they are employed. It is not implied that the variations are pointless, or that the poet is using different counters of precisely the same value but different metrical colours—such different colour is in any case a point of poetical value. Thus *flota* is literally "floater," and is therefore in fact a simple kenning for *boat*; *sund* means "swimming"; *holm* probably "eminence" (the *high* sea); *brim* is properly "breakers, surf." On *beornas* see above p. xv.

This literal version also illustrates other important points. It will be noted that the stop comes normally in the middle of the line. Sense-break and metrical break are usually opposed. This is not so at the beginning, at line 216, and at the end of the passage.

That is because we have in this extract a "verse-period," sub-divided at 216. The previous "period" ended at the end of 209. We then have a transition-phrase, stopped off and occupying one half-line, a not uncommon Old English device. The period describing the journey then proceeds, often in short sentences straddling the line-endings. An exceptionally long passage without a full stop is 217 *departed*—223 *sea-capes*. There is an end-stop at 216 marking the end of the launching and the setting out; and an end-stop marking the end of the period at 228. The next period begins with 229, where the poet turns to the Danish coastguard.

The frequent fall in *significance,* which goes together with the frequent metrical and phonetic fall in stress and pitch, can also be noted at the end of lines. 212, 213, 215, 220, 221, 225, 226, 227, 228 end in finite verbs, 224 in an unemphatic adverb, and 223 in the second element of a compound.

To these may be added *gelīcost* (subordinate to *fugle*) 218. We thus have some 12 "falling" endings out of 19.

The force was renewed and the tone raised at the beginning of the line (as a rule[10]), and there the strongest and heaviest words were usually placed. The more significant elements in the preceding final half-line were frequently caught up and re-echoed

---

[10] After end-stops, such as those in 216, 228, this was not always so. The next line at the head of a period or transition often began with a dip or weak stress and rose at the end. Thus after 216 we get *gewāt*, the highest point in 217 being *wǣg*. After 228 the next period begins with the comparatively rare rising B-pattern: thus 229 *ðā of wéalle geséah* "then from cliff behéld."

or elaborated. Thus 210–11 *boat-boat*; 212–13 *waves-sea*; 214–15 *bright trappings—war-gear well-made*; 221 *land* is elaborated in 222–23 as cliffs by the breaking waves, steep hills, and capes jutting into the sea.

This "parallelism" is characteristic of the style and structure of *Beowulf*. It both favours and is favoured by the metre. It is seen not only in these lesser verbal details, but in the arrangement of minor passages or periods (of narrative, description, or speech), and in the shape of the poem as a whole. Things, actions, or processes, are often depicted by separate strokes, juxtaposed, and frequently neither joined by an expressed link, nor subordinated. The "separate strokes" may be single parallel words: there is no "and" between *flota* 210, *bāt* 211; *strēamas* 212, *sund* 213; *guman* 215, *weras* 216; and similarly 221–23, 226–27. Or sentences: in 224–28 the landing of the men, who moored their ship, while their shirts of mail rang as they moved, is dealt with by separate verbs, unconnected but each with the subject *lēode*. Into this series is inserted, without any connecting word, the short sentence ‖ "shirts rattled, war-raiment"‖.[11] On a larger scale: the strife of the Swedes and Geats in the later part of the poem is dealt with in separate passages, describing prominent incidents on both sides that are not worked into a

---

[11] In this case *hrysedon* is possibly transitive and the subject *leode*. But the unconnected insertion is frequent in undoubted cases. For instance, in 402, where this translation has "the warrior guiding them" (subordinating construction), the original has "they hastened—man guided—under Heorot's roof." Similarly in 405, where the translation reproduces the original unconnected insertion "—— corslet shone——."

narrative sequence. Finally, *Beowulf* itself is like a line of its own verse written large, a balance of two great blocks, A + B; or like two of its parallel sentences with a single subject but no expressed conjunction. Youth + Age; he rose—fell. It may not be, at large or in detail, fluid or musical, but it is strong to stand: tough builder's work of true stone.

J. R. R. TOLKIEN

INTRODUCTION

WHAT follows is an attempt to set down in the simplest and briefest form what is known of the poem, and such inferences from these facts as are generally recognized to have a high degree of probability. As far as possible, theories and hypotheses are avoided, since the most important of these may be explored later by the interested student through the list of works on the poem prefixed to the Notes.

MANUSCRIPT

The only existing MS. of *Beowulf* is contained in a volume of the Cottonian collection in the British Museum, Vitellius A. xv. This volume contains two originally separate codices bound together. Beowulf is the fourth text in the second codex. It is preceded by three prose pieces and followed by *Judith*. The date of the MS. is about the end of the tenth century, judging from the handwriting of the two scribes, and the poem itself probably dates from the early eighth century.

This MS., like so many others, seems to have been picked up after its removal from a monastery at the Dissolution, by one of those Renaissance scholars whose enterprise made the recovery of knowledge of early English literature possible. On the first page of the *Beowulf* MS. is the signature (with date 1563) of

Lawrence Nowell, Dean of Lichfield, whose MS. collections for a projected Anglo-Saxon dictionary are still in the Bodleian Library at Oxford. We next hear of it in the library of the famous bibliophile, Sir Robert Cotton, who died in 1631. It was he who, arranging his MSS. in bookcases each of which was topped by the bust of a Roman emperor, had our *Beowulf* volume catalogued as Vitellius A xv.: and this has remained its designation after its removal to the British Museum in the eighteenth century along with the surviving remains of the Cotton Collection. Meanwhile, however, in 1731 a fire, which destroyed much of this collection, had damaged the book in such a way that later its edges became often broken or otherwise illegible. But in 1787 the Danish scholar, G. J. Thorkelin, had caused a transcript to be made by a professional copyist (known as "Thorkelin A,") and in the same year he himself made another ("Thorkelin B"). These transcripts, made, though clearly with some errors, when the MS. was more legible than it has since become, are a chief source for the reconstruction of the text after the MS. itself.

The *Beowulf* MS. was published in a photographically reproduced facsimile with a transcription and notes by Zupitza for The Early English Text Society in 1882.

ORIGIN OF THE POEM

"*Circa* A.D. 700 " is about as near to a likely date for the composition of *Beowulf* as we can hope to get, failing new and important evidence. The Christian tone, which seems fundamental to this Germanic heroic poem, points to a time not very long after the establishment of the Church in Britain: but at the same time some primitive elements in this Christian tone render it unlikely that *Beowulf* was composed at any very considerable interval after the conversion of England, which was in progress during the first three-quarters of the seventh century. Moreover, the style and technical qualities of the verse point to a date later by a little than Cædmon's extant *Hymn* which we know on the evidence of Bede to have been dictated some time between A.D. 658 and 680. The metre, in which at times an older form of a word or an uncontracted word has to be substituted for the MS. forms to make scansion possible, points to an early date, and yet to one (as has been said above) not much later than Cædmon's *Hymn*. The style too, taken in comparison with all the extant remains of Old English poetry, again seems to point to about this same date of *circa* A.D. 700. The poems of Cynewulf, composed about a century later, show clear evidence of familiarity with *Beowulf*—e.g., especially his *Elene*—while their metre is of a definitely later type.

The probable place of origin for *Beowulf* is somewhere in Northumbria, though there is something perhaps to be said for Western Mercia. The cultural environment necessary for *Beowulf* to have been made as a poem, given our date, seems only to have existed in Northumbria of the age of Bede. There only can one imagine a poet of the education and associations of the author of *Beowulf* to have lived—a man of keen antiquarian interests, with some Classical knowledge (at least of Virgil), not ignorant of the scriptures (especially the Old Testament), and familiar with a highly cultivated and aristocratic life in which poetry was a highly-developed technical entertainment. How great had been the cultural development of Northumbria can be seen from the many artistic monuments which have survived—the Ruthwell Cross, the Bewcastle Column, the Lindisfarne Gospels MS. and the immense advances in knowledge and the capacity for objective historical study implicit in Bede's *Ecclesiastical History*. Nowhere else in Britain at any point in the early Anglo-Saxon period do we know of the production of such work.

Yet it is worth noting that, of the characters in the poem connected with England (practically the whole of the material belongs originally to the Germanic mainland), Offa, in the episode beginning at line 1931 (named in lines 1949 and 1957) was the king of the Continental Angles from whom the Old English kings of Mercia (notably the great Offa of the later eighth century) were descended. Why should a Northumbrian noble audience listen to the tale of Offa the Mercians' ancestor? But connexions by marriage between the royal families of Northumbria and Mercia were not unknown, and are perhaps attested by the Bewcastle Column inscription. The other English characters, Hengest and Finn, in the episode beginning at line 1068, if they are accepted as historical, could only belong, however, to Kent as far as their later history in England is concerned.

Now King Alfred found it necessary to get learned helpers for his educative translations—in so far as he could get them at all in his own country—from West and N.W. Mercia: Wærferth from Worcester and Plegmund from Cheshire: and there is evidence in the *Vespasian Psalter Gloss* (made in Canterbury about the year 870 ultimately from a West Mercian original) that there was a well-established tradition of glossing the Psalms in West Mercia as early as the later eighth century. When the written alliterative poetry seemed to cease after the Norman conquest for a time, it was mainly in the West Midlands and the adjacent Northern parts that its continuant appeared in the later fourteenth century with great artistic power, and with some survivals of the old heroic elaborate diction and technique of words. Perhaps, then, it would not be wise to assume that the absence of tangible monuments of a Mercian culture proves that such a civilisation never existed. Moreover, it was only in parts of these same West Midlands that there was some clear continuity of the highest Anglo-Saxon cultural traditions surviving far into the Middle English period.

Enough has been said to indicate that if *Beowulf* had its origin in Mercia, it was probably in one of its Western areas. The dialect of the original poem, which to some small extent may be discerned through its copying into the Classical literary West-Saxon

D

some three centuries later, was Anglian; that is to say, equally either Northumbrian or Mercian. But the assumption of a Northumbrian origin must remain clearly the more probable view, since it requires far less speculative conjecture than the West Mercian origin.

SOURCES

The material of the poem is primarily Germanic— that is to say, brought from the Germanic mainland by the invaders of Britain and in some degree comprising ideals and subject-matter surviving as a living tradition from the Germanic heroic age. Beowulf himself, whose name has never been entirely explained, may be taken to have been the embodiment of an inherited heroic character, despite the miraculous tales narrated of him in our poem. We do not consider Richard I of England a purely fictional character because of the monstrous fictions told of him by medieval romancers: nor need we reject Beowulf as wholly unhistorical because of his supernatural gifts. Many of the other characters, such as the members of the Danish royal family and the Swedish princes mentioned in the later part of *Beowulf*, are known to history as well as legend in the later-preserved Scandinavian material and the writings of the twelfth century historian of the Danes, Saxo Grammaticus.

It is hard to believe that an Anglo-Saxon aristocratic audience, expecting poetic tales of the Germanic heroes whom they knew as vividly inherited tradition, would have tolerated a Hengest and a Finn unheard of in their inherited history: and the strength of the tradition of Hengest at least, in medieval English poetry and chronicle, seems to corroborate the view that the Hengest of the poem is that same hero who, with his brother Horsa, conquered Kent in the middle of the fifth century after having had in Denmark the adventures described or alluded to in the Finn episode of *Beowulf*. Offa, the other character connected with England, has already been mentioned. Only Unferth, of the non-English characters in the poem seems to have been largely created by the poet to conform to a well-established Germanic heroic convention parallel to the "bad counsellor" at the king's court of tradition: for his name has nowhere been found outside *Beowulf*, though his function in the poem is clear enough as a foil to the hero.

The episodes of the poem, which serve to heighten the tragic expectancy by parallels or contrasts to the main recorded events or to anticipate known disasters and thus to intensify the tragic atmosphere, or to illustrate some trait in the hero's character not well shown in the principal story, are all to some extent paralleled elsewhere. The Finn episode is handled in the surviving later fragment, *The Fight at Finnesburg*, based indirectly on a lost poem even older by its style than *Beowulf*. The Sigemund episode (lines 874ff.) treats of a dragon-slaying tale told and retold later in Scandinavian verse and prose as well as in Middle High German; and though nothing to do with the narrative of Beowulf's life and heroism, it anticipates by a kind of tragic irony the fact that he too will one day slay a treasure-guarding dragon and that upon him too will be accomplished the curse foredoomed to him who should take that treasure. The story of Ingeld of the Heathobards (lines 2024ff.) is again a common Germanic heroic tragedy which deepens the air of fated impending doom which broods over the poem. This tale of Ingeld, like others woven into *Beowulf* for artistic ends, was once a separate heroic poem: for it was to rebuke the fondness for it of the Northumbrian monks that Alcuin sent them the famous rhetorical question "Quid Hinieldus cum Cristo?"

Beowulf is, then, a Germanic heroic poem embodying the inherited Germanic traditions and exalting the Germanic heroic ideals: it can in no way be regarded as an English "national epic", though the presentation of its Germanic themes is coloured by something acquired or developed in England. But besides its historical and heroic legendary elements, its sources are to some extent to be sought in Germanic folklore —Grendel and his mother, the mysterious evil lake of black waters, or the youthful sluggishness of Offa which (like that of the traditional Danish Holger), turned at the proper time into heroic and people-saving virtue and parallels the career of the young Beowulf.

What is often called the "Christian colouring" of the poem is, in fact, fundamental to it, and arises naturally from the circumstances of its origin and composition. A Christian poet addressing a Christian audience, yet sharing with that audience a deep interest in history, legend and tradition, and presenting the inherited Germanic heroic ideals in an inherited poetical diction, would not go out of his way to include anything *specifically* Christian: yet for him as for his listeners, the traditional ideals and ways of life must inevitably be "coloured" by the new Christian Latin culture. Only the long homily of Hrothgar to Beowulf on kingship (lines 1724ff.) and occasional minor moralizings suggest anything like Christian didacticism. But the heroic ideal inherited from pagan Germanic days, though everywhere implicit and often explicit, is touched by Christian ways of thought, and Beowulf at the close is described as: —

> manna mildust ond wyruldcyninga monðwærust,
> leodum liðost ond lofgeornost.

"Men said that, among the kings of the world, he was the kindest and gentlest of men, mildest to his people, and the most eager for fame." The final epithet is pagan Germanic, but the others seem clearly to be the result of Christianity.

The keen antiquarian interests which the poet shared with his audience are shown, apart from the use of the common Germanic material, in the care he takes in recalling the things of the older pagan life no longer in use when the poem was composed, such as the ship-burial of Scyld (lines 28ff.) and the funeral rites of Beowulf himself (lines 3137ff.), though the descriptions contain errors or misconceptions which

archæologists have pointed out. New life and interest
has been given to the ship-funeral described in the
poem by the wonderful finds from an actual ship-
burial which took place for an East Anglian king at
the beginning of the seventh century at Sutton Hoo
in Suffolk, which include some of the treasures placed
on the ship (see the *British Museum Quarterly* for
1939, and *Antiquity,* vol. XIII for September, 1939).

Yet in all this wealth of history, legend, myth,
folk-lore and archæology, there is only one
historical event referred to markedly and repeatedly
in the poem which can be definitely dated and
exactly supported by evidence from outside it. This
is Hygelac's last and fatal raid against the Franks
and Frisians (lines 1202ff.) which took place for
certain about the year A.D. 520. Gregory of Tours,
writing his *Historia Francorum* towards the end of
the sixth century, tells part of the story of the raid,
and this is repeated and amplified by a *Gesta regum
Francorum* and a *Liber Monstrorum* in the eighth
century. These authorities give a Latin name
Chochilaicus (with variants) for Hygelac, which
clearly represents the older Germanic form of the
name, **Hugilaikaz,* which would have been current
in the early sixth century, when Hygelac as a historical king of the Geats of South Sweden, in fact,
reigned. It is this date, *circa* A.D. 520, which must be
the starting-point for all historical study of *Beowulf.*

LANGUAGE

As has been said, the text available to the student

can only be based on the unique MS. which was copied near the close of the tenth century, at a time when the poem had been in use for well nigh three centuries. We have only a few scattered fragments to tell us what the dialects of Northumbria were like at the time when the poem was made, and for Mercian we have not even so much. It is, therefore, quite hopeless for the "experts" to reconstruct the original forms of *Beowulf* as they were first dictated or written down in the early eighth century. But, on the other hand, there is reason to believe that—despite the great fire which so much damaged the MS. in the eighteenth century—the text of the poem has been unusually well preserved: and apart from the transcribing of the words into the forms current in literary English of the days of King Ethelred the Unready and occasional rendering of the metre defective thereby, we probably still possess *Beowulf* in a form in which its great poetic qualities are substantially unchanged.

A kind of literary West-Saxon became the common language of culture in England in the century and a half preceding the Norman conquest: and it is in this literary *koiné* that practically the whole of our early Anglo-Saxon poetry is preserved. As the Norsemen had devastated most of the monasteries (the natural centres of literary culture) in Eastern and Northern England, most of this Classical Anglo-Saxon, as we may call the common literary language of the surviving monuments, shows a Western colouring in its forms or spellings, since only in the S.W.

Midlands and the S.W. of England did good centres
for the copying of MSS. generally exist latterly: and
this was especially true of the late tenth and early
eleventh centuries, the times of greatest activity in
English book-making or remaking. We have, therefore, in *Beowulf,* a poetic inherited vocabulary and
all the traditional technical features of earliest Old
English poetry: but the shapes and spellings are
usually those of the Classical common literary
language of "the golden age of English book-
production". Every now and then, however, the more
advanced student will find forms in the MS. which
seem to point to a much earlier form of the Anglian
dialect, to metrically necessary "de-contraction" of
the later contracted words, or to magic words like
regnheard (326) and *ealuscerwen* (769), which must
have been already archaic and confined to traditional
poetry even when *Beowulf* was first recited.

A number of *early West Saxon*—that is to say of
the time of Alfred—forms suggest that a text was
revised in the time of King Alfred who did so much
to preserve the older poetry. Cf., for examples,
meahte (243), *geaf* (1719), etc. But we know that
there was a text much earlier than the probable King
Alfred recension: for archaic forms, like the instrumental sing. *wundini* (1382) and the fairly frequent
spelling confusion between d and ð (*að* for *ad* of
1107, *drysmaþ* for *ðrysmaþ* of 1375, etc.) point to
the existence of a copy of *Beowulf* as early as the
later eighth century. But enough has been said to
indicate the kind of evidence which might be used

in the attempt to explain the textual history of the poem.

ARGUMENT OF THE POEM

Part I. The exploits of Beowulf in Denmark

1. THE FIGHT WITH GRENDEL

Introductory (lines 1–188).—The poem opens with the story of Scyld, the founder of the Scylding dynasty of the Danes. He came alone over the sea as a helpless child, and after a glorious reign, was sent forth again at his death into the power of the ocean. It is during the reign of his descendant Hrothgar that the events narrated in the first part of the poem take place. Hrothgar built a mighty hall called Heorot, but only for a short time was he able to enjoy it with his people. The monster Grendel, angered by the sounds of rejoicing, came by night and killed thirty of the Danes. For twelve years he continued his ravages—no retainer could defeat him in battle, and no counsellor find a remedy.

Beowulf's voyage and reception in Denmark (lines 189–661).—Beowulf, nephew of Hygelac, king of the Geats, heard of Grendel's ravages, and resolved to go to the assistance of Hrothgar. Wise men among his people encouraged him, and, together with fourteen companions, he set sail. They arrived in Denmark, and were challenged by the coast-warden: but after Beowulf had declared his errand, they were allowed to pass in peace, and were brought to Hrothgar. Wulfgar announced them to the king, who received them graciously. Beowulf explained his purpose in seeking out Hrothgar, and the king spoke of the grief and humiliation caused by Grendel. He invited the Geats to take part in a banquet. While they were feasting, Unferth, a Danish courtier, taunted Beowulf about his swimming-match with Breca. Beowulf told the true story of the contest and predicted his victory over Grendel. In answer to the courteous greeting of Queen Wealhtheow, he expressed his determination to free Heorot from the nightly terror of Grendel or to die.

The watch for Grendel and the fight (lines 662–836).—At nightfall the Danes left the hall, and the Geats remained to keep watch. Grendel came from the moors; he smashed open the door of the hall and quickly seized and devoured a sleeping warrior, Hondscioh. But when he attacked Beowulf, he found himself in the power of a grip mightier than his own. So fierce was the struggle that the hall seemed as though it would fall to the ground. Grendel was eager to escape; but only after his hand and arm had been torn off, was he able to flee away to his joyless dwelling, mortally wounded.

Rejoicing after the defeat of Grendel (lines 837–1250)—In the morning many a warrior followed the tracks of Grendel and rode to the blood-stained mere where he had plunged to his death. They returned, praising Beowulf and listening to the lays of a warrior who recounted the stories of Sigemund and Heremod. Hrothgar went to the hall and gazed on the hand and arm of Grendel hung up as a trophy. He thanked God

for the destruction of his enemy, praised the deed of
Beowulf, and promised him rewards. Beowulf replied,
and described the fight. A great banquet was prepared
in the hall, at which presents were given to Beowulf
and his followers. A minstrel told the story of Finnesburg. Wealhtheow went around the hall; she gave
costly gifts to Beowulf, and begged his kindness for
her sons. After the banquet Hrothgar and the Geats
departed from the hall, which was left in the keeping
of the Danish warriors.

2. THE FIGHT WITH GRENDEL'S MOTHER

Attack by Grendel's mother (lines 1251–1320).—
That night Grendel's mother came to avenge her son.
She found the Danes sleeping, and carried off
Æschere, a favourite retainer of Hrothgar, and her
son's arm. In the morning the king, sad at heart,
sent for Beowulf.

Speeches of Hrothgar and Beowulf (lines 1321–
1398).—Hrothgar lamented the death of Æschere.
He described the terrible mere from whence the
monsters came—a place so haunted and desolate that
even the hunted stag would rather die than take
refuge there. Beowulf at once expressed his readiness
to seek out the monster.

*Expedition to the mere and the fight with Grendel's
mother* (lines 1399–1590).—With a company of
Danes and Geats, the king and Beowulf went to the
lake. After a parting speech, Beowulf plunged into
the water. Grendel's mother took him to her cavern
at the bottom of the lake; but although he was

attacked by many monsters, his armour defended him. His sword failed him in the hour of need, and he was almost overcome when he saw among the weapons hanging in the hall an ancient giant sword, with which he slew the monster. He found Grendel there lying dead, and cut off his head with the sword.

Sequel to the fight (lines 1591–1650).—The Danes gazed on the bloodstained water and gave up hope of Beowulf's return. They went away; but the Geats still waited. After he had cut off Grendel's head, Beowulf saw the sword melt in the blood. There were many treasures in the hall, but he brought away only the hilt of the sword and Grendel's head. He was greeted with rejoicing by the Geats, and together they all went back to Heorot.

Speeches by Beowulf and Hrothgar and the parting next morning (lines 1651–1887).—Beowulf told the story of his struggle. Hrothgar replied by a lengthy moralizing discourse in which Beowulf is contrasted with Heremod. There was joy and feasting in Heorot. Next morning the Geats prepared to depart. Beowulf made a parting speech, and Hrothgar in reply foretold that in the future he would probably be called on to rule over the Geats. The king was overcome with grief at his departure.

3. BEOWULF'S HOMECOMING

Homeward voyage and reception by Hygelac (lines 1888–2199).—The warriors embarked, and in course of time reached the land of the Geats. They went to the court of Hygelac. The mention of the young queen

Hygd leads the poet to tell the story of the haughty and cruel Thryth, with whom he contrasts Hygd. Beowulf described his adventures to Hygelac, and told him what he thought would be the outcome of the betrothal of Hrothgar's daughter Freawaru to Ingeld, prince of the Heathobards. It was an attempt doomed to failure to bring to an end an old feud. He shared with Hygelac and Hygd the treasures brought from Denmark, and received gifts in return. Great honour was accorded him in the land of the Geats.

Part II. Beowulf's fight with the dragon and death.

The robbing of the hoard and the dragon's vengeance (lines 2200–2323).—After the death of Hygelac (while on a raid against the Franks) Beowulf supported his son Heardred, who was killed in the wars with the Swedes. For fifty years Beowulf ruled over the Geats. Then it happened that the hoard of a dragon was robbed by a fugitive slave, and in revenge the monster devastated the surrounding countryside. (The former history of the hoard is given in part.)

Preparation for the fight (lines 2324–2537).— Beowulf resolved to fight the dragon himself, and commanded an iron shield to be made for him. The poet reviews his former exploits, including his adventures in Denmark and on the expeditions in which Hygelac and Heardred lost their lives. With eleven companions he set out for the dragon's cave. In a long speech he recalled the days of his youth, especially the affairs of the Geatish royal house and the wars with the Swedes. He commanded his companions to wait for him while he fought alone with the dragon.

Fight with the dragon and death of Beowulf (lines 2538–2820).—He called out to the dragon and attacked him boldly, but was overwhelmed by the flames, and his sword failed him in his great need. His retainers fled into a wood, all but Wiglaf, who reproached them for their cowardice and ingratitude, and went to the help of his kinsman and lord. He struck the dragon a fatal blow, and Beowulf cut him in two. The dragon died, but the king too had received a mortal wound. He bade Wiglaf bring treasure from the hoard, and, gazing upon it, gave thanks that he had won it for his people. Then he commanded that a high mound should be built on Hronesnes in his memory, bequeathed his armour to Wiglaf, the last of his race, and so died.

Announcement of Beowulf's death and preparation for the funeral (lines 2821–3136).—Sad at heart, Wiglaf rebuked the other ten for their cowardice, and sent a messenger to announce the king's death to the people. In a long speech the envoy recalled the past wars with the Franks and Swedes, and foretold the disaster that might be expected when the death of Beowulf was known. The warriors went to the place of the fight—the ancient curse upon the gold had been fulfilled. As Wiglaf commanded, they brought the treasure from the hoard, and carried the body of Beowulf to the headland.

The funeral (lines 3137–3182).—A great funeral pyre was built, and adorned with weapons. The body of Beowulf was burnt amid great lamentation. They erected a royal mound over the place of the pyre, and put on it the treasures that had been bought so dearly. Twelve warriors rode around the mound lamenting, and praising their lord as king and warrior.

PART I

A.—*BEOWULF AND GRENDEL*

INTRODUCTION

[Lines 1–52]

[The marginal figures refer to the lines of the original.]
*(1–11) The poet begins by referring to the glory
and prowess of the Danish chiefs in ancient tradition.
Of these chiefs, Scyld, who came to the Danes as
a helpless foundling, and gave them their name of
Scyldings, is especially mentioned as a successful
conqueror, and as having subjugated all the neighbouring princes, even those across the sea.*

Lo! We have heard of the glory of the kings
of the people of the Spear-Danes in days of yore
—how those princes did valorous deeds!
Often Scyld scefing took mead-benches away
5 from troops of foes, from many peoples. He
terrified the nobles, after he was first found helpless; he met with consolation for that, increased
under the heavens and throve in honour, until
each one of those who dwelt around, across the
10 whale's road, had to obey him, and to pay him
tribute. A noble king was he!

(12–25) Scyld has a son, Beowulf (not the hero

of the poem), who apparently succeeds him in his old age, when his hold on the reins of power had slackened. The poet moralizes.

Later, a son was born to him, a young child in his courts, whom God sent the people for their help; He perceived the deep distress which
15 they, lacking a lord, long had suffered in the past. To him, therefore, the Prince of Life, the glorious Ruler, granted worldly honour; Beowulf the son of Scyld, was renowned, his fame spread
20 widely in the North-lands. So ought a young man to compass by noble deeds, by liberal gifts in his father's possession, that afterwards, in later years, willing companions may stand by him—that men may do him service when war comes. By commendable deeds a man shall
25 thrive in every people!

(26–52) So Scyld, about to die after a long reign, was at his own request taken to the sea-shore by his retainers, and sent off to sea in a ship adorned with costly armour and other things, to do him honour, as was meet for a true sea-king and one who, as a child, had been put out to sea alone in like manner.

Then, at the fated hour, Scyld, a man most valorous, departed, to go into the keeping of the Lord; his beloved friends carried him to the sea's flood, as he himself had asked when he,

E

30 protector of the Scyldings, still ruled them with
his words. Dear prince of his country, for long
he reigned. There, at the landing-place, the
ring-prowed vessel lay, the prince's ship, covered
with ice and eager to start. They laid then
35 the beloved chieftain, giver of rings, on the
ship's bosom, glorious by the mast. There were
brought many treasures, ornaments from far-off
lands. Never have I heard that a vessel was more
fairly fitted-out with war-weapons and battle-
40 raiment, swords and coats of mail. On his bosom
lay a host of treasures, which were to travel far
with him into the power of the flood. They
furnished him with no lesser gifts, and royal
45 treasures, than those had done who, in the beginning, sent him forth over the sea alone, child as
he was. They set besides a golden standard high
above his head, and let the sea bear him,—gave
50 him to the ocean. Their soul was sad, their spirit
sorrowful. Counsellors in hall, mighty men
beneath the heavens cannot say truly who
received that load.

I

THE HALL HEOROT

[Lines 53–114]

(53–63) *After the passing of Scyld, Beowulf the
Dane reigned a long time, and a son, Healfdene,
was born to him, who ruled well and in turn had*

*four children—Heorogar, Hrothgar and Halga
(sons), and a daughter, who married a Swedish chieftain.*

Then in the strongholds was Beowulf of the
Scyldings, dear king of the nation, long time
55 renowned among peoples,—the prince his father
had gone elsewhere from the earth,—until the
noble Healfdene was born to his home. While
he lived, old and fierce in battle, he ruled the
gracious Scyldings. To him, the leader of armies,
60 were born into the world four children in succession, Heorogar and Hrothgar and Halga the
Good. I have been told that (. . . was On)ela's
queen, the cherished consort of the warrior-
Scylfing.

*(64–73) Hrothgar was a victorious and renowned
prince, and was minded to build a huge hall for
feasting, in which he could also deal out gifts to his
men.*

Then was success in war granted to Hrothgar,
65 glory in battle, so that the men of his house
served him willingly, till the young warriors
increased, a mighty troop of men.

It came into his mind that he would order
men to build a hall, a house of feasting (greater)
70 than the sons of men had ever heard of—and
therewithin he would apportion all things to
young and old, whatever God had given him,
except public land and the lives of men.

*(74–81)   Many men were impressed for this
service, and the hall was quickly finished. Hrothgar
named it Heorot and made it a place of banqueting
and gift-bestowing, as he had promised.*

Then I heard that orders for the work were
75 given far and wide to many a nation throughout
this earth to adorn the people's hall.   In time—
quickly among men—it befell that it was all
ready—the greatest of houses. He who by his
word had ruled far and wide, devised for it the
80 name of Heorot. He did not break his promise,
but gave out rings and treasure at the banquet.

*(81–85)   The poet hints that the Hall was even-
tually destroyed by fire, and refers obscurely to the
episode of Ingeld and Freawaru.*

The hall towered high, lofty and wide-gabled,
—it awaited the hostile surges of malignant fire.
Nor was the time yet near at hand that cruel
85 hatred between son-in-law and father-in-law
should arise, because of a deadly deed of violence.

*(86–101)   The daily revelry in hall enrages an evil
monster, Grendel.*

Then the mighty spirit who dwelt in darkness
bore grievously a time of hardship, in that
he heard each day loud revelry in hall ;—there
90 was the sound of the harp, the clear song of
the minstrel.

He who could recount the first making of men
from distant ages, spoke. He said that the
Almighty made the earth, a fair and bright plain,
which water encompasses, and, triumphing in
95 power, appointed the radiance of the sun and
moon as light for the land-dwellers, and decked
the earth-regions with branches and leaves. He
fashioned life for all the kinds that live and
move.

So those brave men lived prosperously in joy,
100 until one began to compass deeds of malice.

*(102–114) Like all other monsters, he was of the
brood of Cain, and dwelt, an outcast spirit, among
the moors and fens.*

That grim spirit was called Grendel, the
renowned traverser of the marches, who held
105 the moors, the fen and fastness; unblessed creature, he dwelt for a while in the lair of monsters,
after the Creator had condemned them. On
Cain's kindred did the everlasting Lord avenge
the murder, for that he had slain Abel; he had
no joy of that feud, but the Creator drove him
110 far from mankind for that misdeed. Thence all
evil broods were born, ogres and elves and evil
spirits—the giants also, who long time fought
with God, for which he gave them their reward.

II

[Lines 115–188]

(115–120) Grendel prowls about at night, to see how the Danes bestow themselves after the banquet, and he finds a band of warriors asleep within the hall, secure and happy.

115   So, after night had come, Grendel went to the lofty house, to find how the Ring-Danes had disposed themselves in it after their ale-drinking. Then found he therewithin a band of noble warriors, sleeping after the banquet; they knew not sorrow, the sad lot of mortals.

(120–125) He swoops down on thirty men and carries them off to his lair.

120   Straightway the grim and greedy creature of damnation, fierce and furious, was ready, and seized thirty thanes in their resting-place. Thence he went back again, exulting in plunder, 125 journeying home, to seek out his abode with that fill of slaughter.

(126–134) At dawn the foul deed comes to light; there is weeping and wailing. King Hrothgar's grief is deep.

Then in the morning light, at break of day,

Grendel's strength in war was manifest to men;
then was a cry, a mighty noise at morn, upraised
130 after the feasting. The famous prince, the prince
well known of old, sat downcast. Strong in might
he suffered, endured sorrow for his lieges, when
they surveyed the traces of the foe, the accursed
spirit; that strife was too strong, too hateful and
long-lasting.

(*134–146*) *On the next night Grendel comes
again and commits further outrages. Hence the hall
is deserted by the sleepers, and Grendel is master
of it.*

135   There was no longer respite, but after one
night he again wrought greater deeds of murder,
violence and outrage, and had no regret therefore—he was too deep in them. Then was
the man easy to find who sought elsewhere more
remote a resting-place for himself, a bed among
140 the out-buildings, when the hall-warden's hate
had been declared to him, and truthfully made
known by a clear token. He who escaped the
fiend kept himself afterwards farther off and
more secure.

In this way he was master, and strove,
145 opposed to right, one against all; until the best
of houses stood deserted.

(*146–158*) *For twelve whole years Hrothgar
suffered grief and humiliation. Grendel could neither
be overcome nor redress got for his deeds.*

It was a long while: twelve winters' space the
Scyldings' lord endured distress—every kind of
woe, deep sorrows. Therefore it was then with-
150 out concealment made known to sons of men—
sadly in song—that Grendel fought for a long
time against Hrothgar,—waged hate-begotten
feuds, outrage and enmity for many seasons—
continual strife; he would not make peace with
155 any man of the Danish host, nor cease from
murder of the counsellors there, nor make a lawful compensation; and none need look for a
handsome reparation at the slayer's hands.

*(159–169) Night after night the grisly horrors
continue, and Grendel keeps possession of the hall.*

But the demon, the dark death-shadow, ever
160 pursued young and old; laid in wait for and en-
trapped them. In the endless night he held the
misty moors,—men know not where such mysterious creatures of hell go in their wanderings.
So many outrages, severe afflictions, did the
165 foe of man, the fearful solitary, achieve in quick
succession. He held Heorot, the hall adorned
with treasure, on the dark nights. He could
not approach the throne, nor receive a gift
because of the Lord; He did not take thought
of him.

(170–188) Time passed on, councils were held,

sacrifices were made at the shrines of idols, but the disaster to the nation did not cease.

(The fact was, says the poet, that they were woe- fully in the wrong with their devil-worship; they knew nothing of the true God.)

170   That was great heart-breaking sorrow to the guardian of the Scyldings. Many a mighty one sat oft in council, sought for a wise plan,—what it were best for men of courage to contrive against the sudden terrors. Sometimes they 175 vowed sacrifices at the tabernacles of idols,— prayed aloud that the destroyer of souls would provide them help against the distress of the people. Such was their custom,—the hope of 180 the heathen,—they remembered hellish things in the thoughts of their hearts. They knew not the Creator, Judge of deeds; they knew not the Lord God, nor, truly, had they learned to wor- ship the Protector of the heavens, the glorious Ruler.

   Woe shall it be to him who is destined in dire 185 distressful wise to thrust his soul into the fire's embrace, to hope for no comfort, in no way to change.

   Weal shall be his, who may after his death- day stand before the Lord, and seek peace in the Father's arms!

III

[Lines 189–257]

(189–198) *At last it came to pass that while Hrothgar was brooding over the nation's evil case, Beowulf, a valiant thane of Hygelac, King of the Geats, heard in his own country of the deeds of Grendel.*

Thus the son of Healfdene brooded constantly
190 over the trouble of this time. The wise prince could not ward off the distress; the strife which had befallen the people, the fiercely grim, dire persecution, greatest of evils that come by night, was too severe, too hateful and long-lasting. A
195 thane of Hygelac, excellent among the Geats,—he who was strongest of mankind in might in this life's day, noble and stalwart,—heard in his fatherland of Grendel's deeds.

(198–209) *So he determined to take ship and offer his services to Hrothgar, and in this he was encouraged even by the more prudent warriors. A band of fourteen lusty men-at-arms went with him.*

He bade make ready for himself a good ship for the crossing of the waves,—said he would
200 seek the warrior-king, the noted prince, over the swan's-road, since he was in need of men. Wise men did not blame him at all for that expedition,

though he was dear to them; they urged on the
stout-hearted one, and watched the omens. The
205 hero had chosen warriors from the people of the
Geats, from the boldest he could find; with
fourteen men he went to the ship; skilled in
sea-craft, he himself led the way to the shore.

(210–228) *Here follows a graphic picture of the
embarkation, the voyage and the landing—one of the
gems of the poem. The party thank God for their
prosperous journey.*

210   Time passed on; the bark was on the waves,
the boat under the lee of the cliff. The warriors,
well prepared, stepped on to the prow; streams
of ocean made the sea eddy against the sand;
215 men bore into the bosom of the ship bright
armour, splendid war-gear; the heroes, the
warriors on their eagerly-sought adventure,
pushed off the vessel of braced timbers. Then
with foam at its prow, most like to a bird, it
floated over the billowing waves, urged onwards
220 by the wind, until in due time on the second day
the curved prow had journeyed on so far that
the voyagers saw the land, the sea-cliffs, glisten
—the steep mountains, the bold promontories.
Then was the ship at the end of its watery way.
225   After that the people of the Geats went
quickly up on to dry land; they made fast the
ship; their coats of mail, their armour, rang; they
thanked God that for them the sea-paths had
been easy.

(229–257) *The Danish coast-warden, bursting
with curiosity, sees the party unloading their imple-
ments of war. He hurriedly rides down to the shore,
challenges the newcomers, spear in hand, explains his
office, and asks the company who they are, and
what their business is. He observes that the whole band
come in no peaceful guise, and that one of them
(Beowulf, no doubt) is to all appearance a person of
distinction.*

Then from the rampart the watchman of the
230 Scyldings, who had to guard the sea-cliffs, saw
them lift bright shields and trim war-harness
over the gangway. In the thoughts of his mind
he was tormented with curiosity as to who these
235 men were. Then he, Hrothgar's officer, went
off riding his horse to the shore; mightily he
shook the strong spear-shaft in his hands, and
asked in formal words: "What kind of armed
"men are ye, clad in coats of mail, who have
"thus come and brought a towering ship over
"the water-ways, hither over the seas? For a
240 "long time I have been acting as coast-guard,
"I kept watch over the shore, so that on Danish
"land no enemy might do us harm with a
"force coming by sea. No strangers have ever
245 "begun to land here more openly with their
"shields,—nor were ye at all sure of the consent
"of men-at-arms, the permission of kinsmen.
"Never have I seen a mightier noble upon earth,
"a warrior in armour, than is one of you; that is

250 "no retainer dignified by weapons, unless his
"countenance, his peerless form, belies him.

"Now, I must know your lineage, ere ye go
"further, as faithless spies, on Danish ground.
255 "Now, ye strangers from far, ye sea-traversers,
"hear my plain opinion;—it is best to tell me
"quickly the cause of your coming!"

IV

THE ERRAND TOLD

[Lines 258–319]

(258–272) *To him Beowulf makes answer that he
and his party are Geats, from Hygelac's court; that he
himself is the son of Ecgtheow, a famous chief; and
that they have all come on a special and friendly
mission to Hrothgar.*

To him answered the leader of the band, the
260 chieftain of the troop unlocked his store of
words:—"We are people of the Geatish nation
"and hearth-companions of Hygelac. My father
"was renowned among peoples, a noble leader in
"battle named Ecgtheow. He tarried many win-
265 "ters before he, an old man, passed away from
"the dwellings of men; each of the wise men far
"and wide throughout the earth recalls him
"readily. We have come to seek thy lord, the
"son of Healfdene, the protector of the people,
"with honourable intent; give us good counsel!

270 "We have a great errand to the famous ruler
"of the Danes, nor shall aught of it be kept
"secret, as I think."

*(272–285) Beowulf has heard that some secret
devastator has set up a reign of terror among the
Danes, and he can offer Hrothgar good counsel on the
great question whether this scourge is ever to cease
or not.*

"Thou knowest if it is so, as truly we heard
"it said, that among the Scyldings some foeman,
275 "some secret ravager, shows in terrible wise in
"the dark nights malignity untold, carnage and
"crushing shame. I can give Hrothgar good
"counsel about this, with generous mind,—how
"he, the wise and good, shall overcome the
280 "fiend"; if, said Beowulf, for him there should
ever come a change and help from the torment
of afflictions, and the surges of care grow cooler;
or else he should ever hereafter endure a time of
tribulation—crushing misery, long as the best
285 of houses lasts there in its lofty place.

*(286–300) The coast-warden accepts these friendly
assurances, and allows the little band to pass on,
armed. He is even well disposed enough to promise
to set a guard over their ship till they return, and he
ends with a compliment to Beowulf. Such a man will
surely return uninjured from the fray!*

The watchman, bold retainer, answered sitting
there on his horse:—"The bold shield-warrior,
"who judges well, must know the difference be-
"tween these two—words and deeds. I under-
290 "stand that this is a company friendly to the
"lord of the Scyldings. Pass forth, bearing your
"weapons and armour,—I will guide you. More-
"over, I will bid my comrades honourably to
295 "guard your ship against all enemies, your fresh-
"tarred vessel on the beach, until at last the
"wooden craft with twisted prow bears the
"beloved man back to the shore of Geat-land
"over the eddying seas. To one of such noble
"deeds it will be granted that he shall come
300 "safely through the rush of battle."

*(301–319) The troop go on their way, their
armour glistening in the sun, with boar-images
conspicuous on their helmets. Eagerly they advance,
until the hall comes in sight. The coast-warden
points it out to them, commends them to God, and
departs.*

They set out then to journey on;—the ship
remained still, the spacious vessel rode on the
painter, held by its anchor. Above the cheek-
guards shone the boar-images, covered with
305 gold, gleaming and tempered. The fierce-hearted
boar held guard over the warlike men. The
warriors hastened; they went together until they
could descry the timbered hall, splendid and

gold-adorned, which was for men dwelling on
this earth the most famous of buildings under
310 heaven;—in this the ruler dwelt,—its radiance
gleamed o'er many lands. Then did the warrior
bold in battle point out to them the radiant
dwelling of brave men, that they might go
315 straight thither. The mighty war-hero turned
his horse, and then he spoke these words:—"It
"is time for me to depart. May the Almighty
"Father keep you safe in your adventures by
"His grace. I will go to the sea, to keep ward
"against hostile bands."

V

BEOWULF AND WULFGAR

[Lines 320–370]

(320–331) *Arrived at the hall, they pile arms and*
sit down.

320 The road was paved, the path guided the men
together. When they first went to the hall in
their dread armour, each corslet glittered, hard
and linked by hand, the gleaming rings of iron
325 clinked in their harness. Sea-weary, they put
their broad shields, their bucklers wondrous hard,
against the palace wall; then they seated themselves upon the bench; the corslets, war-dress of
the heroes, rang; the spears were piled together,
the armour of the sea-men,—the ash spear, grey

330 at the tip. The troop clad in mail was well
furnished with weapons.

*(331–339) Wulfgar, a prince of the Wendels, and
herald of King Hrothgar, asks whence the strangers
have come. He admires their war-gear and concludes
that they have visited Hrothgar, not as fugitives and
exiles, but for some brave purpose.*

There, then, a proud and mighty man questioned the warriors concerning their lineage : —
"Whence have ye brought these plated shields,
"these hauberks, grey and visored helmets,
335 "this pile of battle-shafts? I am Hrothgar's
"herald and officer. I have never seen so many
"foreigners more bold. I believe you have
"sought out Hrothgar, not from exile, but from
"prowess and from loftiness of spirit!"

*(340–347) In reply Beowulf gives his name ; says
that he and his fellows are from Hygelac's court,
and asks leave to tell his errand to Hrothgar in
person.*

340 Then the man renowned in strength answered
him ; the proud leader of the Geats, hardy under
his helmet, rejoined in speech: "We are Hy-
"gelac's table-companions. Beowulf is my name.
"I wish to tell my errand to the son of Healf-
345 "dene, the famous prince thy master, if he will
"grant us that we may speak with his gracious
"self."

F

(*348–355*) *Wulfgar promises to report this request to Hrothgar and to bring back his answer.*

Wulfgar replied (he was a chief of the Wendels; his courageous mind, his prowess and wis-
350 dom were well known to many): "I will ask the "lord of the Danes, the ruler of the Scyldings "and giver of rings, the renowned prince, as "thou makest request, concerning thy expedition, "and will forthwith announce to thee the answer
355 "which the noble leader thinks fit to give me."

(*356–370*) *Quickly he goes into the presence of his lord, announces the coming of Beowulf and his friends, says they wish for an interview, and begs that it may be granted, being much impressed by the noble bearing of the party.*

Then he returned quickly to where Hrothgar sat, old and hoary, with his suite of nobles;
the valiant one went on until he stood before
the shoulders of the Danish lord,—he knew the
360 usages of noble warriors. Wulfgar spoke to his
beloved lord: "People of the Geats, come from "far, over the seas, have voyaged hither; the "warriors call their chief Beowulf. They make
365 "request that they may now exchange words with "thee, my ruler. Refuse them not thy conversa-
"tion, gracious Hrothgar ! In their war-trappings "they seem worthy of the high esteem of nobles. "Assuredly the chief is doughty who has led
370 "these battle-heroes hither."

VI

[Lines 371–455]

(371–389) Hrothgar recollects Beowulf as a youth, speaks of his parentage and says that a certain embassy from the Danes to the Geats once brought back tidings of his tremendous strength. He surmises that the men have come to help him against Grendel, and tells Wulfgar to bid them welcome and to bring them in.

Hrothgar, the Scyldings' protector, replied:
"I knew him when he was a youth. His honoured
"father was called Ecgtheow: Hrethel the Geat
375 "gave him his only daughter in marriage; his
"son has now come boldly here, and visited a
"trusty friend. Moreover, sea-farers, who carried
"thither costly presents for the Geats as a token
380 "of my esteem, used to say that he, the famed
"in battle, had in his grip of hand the force of
"thirty men. The holy God has of his mercy
"sent him to us West-Danes, as I hope, to meet
385 "the terror of Grendel. I shall proffer the brave
"man treasures for his courage. Do thou make
"haste; bid them come in together to see my
"noble band of kinsfolk. Tell them besides in
"words that they are welcome to the Danish
"people."

(*389-398*) *Wulfgar accordingly invites the Geats
into the presence of his lord. They are allowed to
come in in helm and corslet, but leave their shields
and spears behind.*

390   Then to the hall-door Wulfgar went, and
brought the message from within: "My con-
"quering lord, chief of the Eastern Danes, bade
"me inform you that he knows your noble blood,
"and that ye men of brave intent are welcome to
"him hither over the sea-billows. Now may ye
395 "go and see Hrothgar in your fighting raiment,
"under your helmets; let your battle-shields and
"your wooden spear-shafts await here the issue
"of the parleys."

(*399-404*) *So Beowulf and his comrades go in,
except two or three who are left behind to guard the
weapons. Beowulf himself steps into the hall.*

        Then the mighty chieftain rose with many a
400 warrior round him,—a splendid band of followers; some waited there and guarded the
accoutrements, as the brave man commanded
them. Together they hastened forward under
the roof of Heorot, the warrior guiding them.
The valiant one advanced, hardy under his
helmet, until he stood on the hearth.

(*405-426*) *He greets Hrothgar, says he has heard
of Grendel's evil doings, and has been counselled by*

his countrymen, familiar with his past exploits, to
offer Hrothgar his services. Now he is ready to fight
with the monster single-handed.

405   Beowulf spoke, the corslet on him shone, the
armour cunningly linked by the skill of the
smith: "Hail to thee, Hrothgar! I am Hygelac's
"kinsman and retainer. I have in my youth under-
"taken many deeds of daring. Grendel's doings
410 "became plainly known to me in my fatherland.
"Sea-farers say that this hall, this most noble
"building, stands empty and useless to every
"man after the evening sun has become hidden
415 "under the vault of heaven. Then my people, the
"noble and wise men, advised me thus, lord
"Hrothgar,—that I should visit thee, because
"they knew the strength of my might. They had
"themselves looked on, when, blood-stained
"from battles, I returned from the fight, where I
420 "bound five, laid low a brood of giants, and slew
"by night sea-monsters on the waves; I suffered
"direful straits, and avenged the attacks upon
"the storm-loving Geats—they courted trouble
"—I ground down the fierce foes. And now I
425 "will decide the matter alone against the mon-
"ster, the giant, Grendel!"

    (426–440) As they have come all this way for the
purpose, he hopes Hrothgar will not deny his party
the honour of purging Heorot. For himself, he engages
to renounce his arms, since his foe has none, and he
will not take a mean advantage.

"Now therefore I will beg of thee one boon,
"thou ruler of the glorious Danes, protector of
"the Scyldings. Do not refuse me this, defender
430 "of warriors, beloved lord of peoples, now I am
"come thus far;—that I alone, with my band
"of noble warriors, this troop of doughty men,
"may cleanse Heorot. Moreover, I have learnt
"that in his rashness the monster recks not of
435 "weapons. Hence—so that Hygelac, my prince,
"may be glad at heart on my account, I renounce
"that I should bear a sword, or ample shield, or
"yellow buckler to the battle; but with the fiend
"I will close with grip of hand, and contend for
440 "our lives, foe against foe."

*(440–455) The fighting shall be fair, and then
the vanquished will feel that it is God's judgment.
Beowulf well knows that he must conquer, or die a
ghastly death. If it is his fate to be slain, he begs that
his coat of mail may go to Hygelac. What must be,
must!*

"He whom death carries off shall resign him-
"self to God's judgment. I doubt it not that
"if he may prevail, he will eat fearlessly the
"Geatish people in the hall of battle, as he has
445 "often done the flower of their warriors.
"Thou wilt have no need to cover my head
"in burial; for he will have me covered with
"blood, if death seizes me. He will bear off the
"bloody corpse, will set his mind upon devouring

"it. The lonely one will feast unpityingly, and
450 "stain the hollows of the moor;—no further wilt
"thou need to care about the disposal of my
"corpse. If battle takes me, do thou send Hy-
"gelac this best of war-dresses, most excellent of
"corslets, which protects my breast; it is
"Hrethel's ancestral treasure, the work of
455 "Weland. Fate goes ever as it must!"

VII

HROTHGAR TELLS OF GRENDEL

[Lines 456–498]

*(456–472) Hrothgar recognizes the good inten-
tions of the Geats. He refers to Ecgtheow's history
—how he slew a Wylfing chief, and his own people,
fearing reprisals, would not have him back in
Geatland. So he went to Denmark and took refuge
at the court of Hrothgar, then a young man. The
latter paid the lawful reparation for him to the
Wylfings and so ended the feud, and Ecgtheow, out
of gratitude, swore fealty to him. (This episode may
be inserted to explain why it is natural that
Ecgtheow's son Beowulf should now do Hrothgar
a good turn.)*

Then Hrothgar, protector of the Scyldings,
spoke: "My friend Beowulf, thou hast sought
"us to fight in our defence and for kindly aid.
"Thy father brought about by fight the great-

460 "est of feuds; he was the slayer of Heatholaf
"among the Wylfings; then the people of the
"Geats could not harbour him, from fear of war.
"Thence went he to the people of the South
"Danes, the honoured Scyldings, over the surg-
465 "ing of the waves. I had just begun to rule the
"people of the Danes, held in my younger days
"the stronghold of heroes, my spacious king-
"dom, when Heorogar, my elder brother, the
"son of Healfdene, was dead and lifeless. He
"was better than I! I settled afterwards the feud
470 "with money. I sent ancient treasures over the
"sea's ridge to the Wylfings. Ecgtheow swore
"oaths to me."

*(473–479) No one can tell what havoc Grendel
has wrought. Yet God can put an end to it.*

"It is a grief to me in my heart to tell any
"man what Grendel with his thoughts of
465 "hate has wrought for me in Heorot of harm
"and sudden harassings. My troop in hall, my
"war-band is diminished. Fate has swept them
"off into the fearsome toils of Grendel. God can
"easily restrain the wild ravager from his deeds!"

*(480–490) Often men-at-arms, inspirited by drink,
pledged themselves to wait for Grendel in the hall.
Next morning they were gone, their blood stained the
chamber-floor! He ends with an invitation to the
banquet, at which Beowulf may enjoy entertainment
by a poet.*

480   "Full often fighting men, after the drinking
"of beer, pledged themselves over the ale-cup
"that they would await in the banqueting-hall
"the combat with Grendel with terrible swords.
"Then at morning-time, when day shone forth,
485 "was this mead-hall, this chamber for retainers,
"stained with gore—all the bench-boards deluged
"with blood and gore of swords. Through that
"I had the fewer trusty followers, dear warriors,
"because death had taken them away. Sit now
490 "at the banquet and in due season listen to the
"victorious deeds of heroes, as inclination moves
"thee."

(491–498)   *Soon the flagon was passed round and
the minstrel sang,—Danes and Geats held revel
together.*

Then a bench was cleared in the banqueting-
hall for the men of the Geats, all together;
thither went the bold ones to sit, exulting in
strength. A servant did his office, who bore
495 in his hands a decorated ale-cup, and poured
out the bright liquor. Now and again a minstrel
sang, clear-voiced in Heorot. There was revelry
among the heroes,—no small company of Danes
and Geats.

VIII

UNFERTH TAUNTS BEOWULF

BEOWULF'S CONTEST WITH BRECA

[Lines 499-558]

(499–505) *Now comes a jarring note. Unferth,*
a Danish courtier, is devoured by jealousy, and taunts
Beowulf.

500   Then Unferth, the son of Ecglaf, who sat at
the feet of the lord of the Scyldings, spoke, and
gave vent to secret thoughts of strife. The
journey of Beowulf the brave sea-farer, was a
great chagrin to him; for he grudged that any
other man under heaven should ever obtain more
505 glory on this earth than he himself.

(506–528) *"Art thou the same Beowulf," says he,*
"who ventured on a foolhardy swimming-match with
"Breca on the open sea in winter, for seven days,
"and got beaten? A worse fate is in store for thee
"when thou meetest Grendel!"

    "Art thou that Beowulf who strove with
"Breca, contended with him in the open sea, in
"a swimming-contest, when ye two for vainglory
"tried the floods, and ventured your lives in deep
510 "water for idle boasting? Nor could any man,
"friend or foe, dissuade you from your sorry
"enterprise when ye journeyed on the sea; when

"ye compassed the flowing stream with your
"arms, passed over the paths of the sea, made
515 "quick movements with your hands, and sped
"over the ocean; when the sea, the winter's
"flood, surged with waves. Ye two toiled in the
"water's realm seven nights; he overcame thee
"at swimming: he had greater strength. Then,
"at morning-time, the ocean cast him up on the
520 "Heathorǣmas' land. Thence, dear to his people,
"he sought his beloved fatherland, the land of
"the Brondings, his fair stronghold, where he
"had subjects and treasures and a stronghold.
"The son of Beanstan performed faithfully in
525 "the contest with thee all that he had pledged
"himself to. So I expect from thee a worse
"issue,—though thou hast everywhere prevailed
"in rush of battle, stern war,—if thou darest
"await Grendel at close quarters for the space
"of a night."

(529–558) *Beowulf replies with much warmth,
and gives his own version of the story about Breca.
He and Breca, when young men, dared each other to
a swimming-match on the sea, each taking a naked
sword with which to keep off the whales. They held
together for five days, till cold and darkness and the
high wind drove them apart. Sea-monsters came near,
one of whom attacked Beowulf and dragged him
down. He was, however, protected by his armour,
and despatched the beast.*

529   Beowulf, son of Ecgtheow, replied: "Lo, my
"friend Unferth, thou hast talked a great deal,
"drunken with beer, concerning Breca, and hast
"said much about his adventure! I claim it to
"be true that I had more strength in swim-
"ming, more hard struggle in the waves, than
"any other man.

535   "When we were young men, we two agreed
"and pledged ourselves,—we were both then
"still in the time of youth—that we would ven-
"ture our lives out on the sea; and that we did,
"accordingly. When we swam in the sea we had
540 "a naked sword, rigid in hand;—we thought to
"guard ourselves against whales. He could not
"by any means swim far from me in the surging
"waves, swifter in the sea than I;—I did not
"wish to go from him. Thus we two were
545 "together in the sea for the space of five nights,
"till the flood, the tossing seas, the bitter-cold
"weather, the darkening night, drove us apart,
"and the fierce north wind turned against us,—
"rough were the waves. The wrath of the sea-
550 "fishes was aroused; then my corslet, hard and
"linked by hand, furnished me help against the
"foes; the woven shirt of mail, adorned with
"gold, covered my breast. A hostile deadly brute
"dragged me to the bottom, the grim beast had
555 "me fast in his grip. Still, it was granted to me
"that I might strike the monster with my sword-
"point, with my fighting weapon; the force of
"battle carried off the sea-beast by my hand."

IX

BEOWULF'S CONTEST WITH BRECA CONTINUED.

THE FEAST

[Lines 559–661]

*(559–581)   More of the sea-fiends came on.
Beowulf laid about him with his sword and killed
nine of them. Their mutilated corpses strewed the
shore. Then the sun rose and Beowulf could see the
land. There never was a tougher struggle; but fortune often favours the undoomed brave; and Beowulf
lived through it, and was at last landed by the
current on the shore of the Lapp's country, exhausted,
but safe.*

559   "Thus did the hateful persecutors press me
"hard and often. With my noble sword I served
"them as was fitting. The base destroyers did
"not have the joy of that feast—that they might
"eat me,—sitting round the banquet at the sea-
565   "bottom. But at morning they lay wounded by
"swords, up along the foreshore—slain by battle
"blades—so that henceforth, they could not
"hinder sea-farers in their passage over the deep
"water-way. The sun, bright beacon of God,
570   "came from the east; the waters grew calm, so
"that I could descry sea-headlands, wind-swept
"cliffs. Often Fate saves an undoomed man, if
"his courage is good! Yet it was granted me to
"slay nine sea-monsters with my sword! Never

575 "have I been told of harder struggle at night
    "under the vault of heaven, nor of a man more
    "wretched in the ocean streams. Yet I escaped
    "the grip of the monsters with my life, weary
    "of my enterprise. Then the sea-flood bore me
580 "by its current, the surging ocean, to the land
    "of the Lapps."

(581–601) "I have never," adds Beowulf, "heard
"any such exploits told about you, Unferth! Neither
"you nor Breca are equal to it. It is true you did
"kill your own brothers; but you will have to suffer
"for that in hell, clever as you are. The fact is,
"Grendel would never have wrought such mischief
"if you and your Danish comrades had not been such
"cowards. As it is, he does what he likes, and cares
"not a straw for your warlike Danes."

    "I have never heard such contests, such peril
    "of swords related about thee. Never yet did
585 "Breca at the battle-play, nor either of you, per-
    "form so bold a deed with shining swords. I do
    "not boast much of that; though thou wast the
    "slayer of thy brothers—thy near kinsmen; for
    "that thou shalt suffer damnation in hell, good
590 "though thy skill may be. In truth I tell thee, son
    "of Ecglaf, that Grendel the horrible demon,
    "would never have done so many dread deeds to
    "thy prince, such havoc in Heorot, if thy heart,
    "thy spirit, were as warlike as thou sayest thy-
595 "self. But he has found out that he need not too

"much dread the enmity, the terrible sword-
"storm of your people, the victorious Scyldings.
"He takes toll by force, spares none of the
"Danish people; but he rejoices, kills and
600 "destroys, and cares not for the opposition of
"the Spear-Danes."

(601–606) *"Now I am going to show him what
"Geatish courage is like—and to-morrow every one
"will be able to drink his mead in peace!"*

"Now, however, I shall quickly show him the
"strength and courage, the war-craft of the
"Geats. Afterwards—when the morning-light
605 "of another day, the sun encompassed with light,
"shines from the South over the sons of men—
"he who may shall go boldly to the mead-
"drinking!"

(607–610) *Hrothgar, far from being insulted at
the reflections on his men, rejoices at the prospect of
help.*

Then the giver of treasure, grey-haired and
famed in battle, was in joyful mood; the prince of
the glorious Danes counted on help; the shep-
610 herd of the people heard from Beowulf his firm
resolve.

(611–628) *The revelry proceeds. Wealhtheow,
the queen consort, goes forth and courteously greets*

the guests. After offering the cup to Hrothgar, she goes round the hall with it, handing it to the older and the younger men-at-arms in turn. At last she comes to Beowulf, and thanks God that she may look to him for help against the scourge of the nation.

There was laughter of warriors, song sounded forth, the words were joyous. Wealhtheow, Hrothgar's queen, went forth, mindful of court usage; gold-adorned, she greeted the men in hall,
615 and then the noble woman gave the cup first to the guardian of the land of the East-Danes, and bade him be joyful at the beer-drinking, lovable to his people. He, the victorious king, partook in gladness of the feast and hall-cup.
620 Then the lady of the Helmings went round every part of the hall, to old and young; proffered the costly goblet; until the time came that she, the diademed queen, ripe in judgment, bore the
625 mead-cup to Beowulf. She greeted the prince of the Geats, and, discreet in speech, thanked God that her desire had been fulfilled, that she might look to some warrior for help from these attacks.

(628-641) Beowulf replies that he will conquer or die, much to the delight of Wealhtheow, who goes back to sit by the side of the king.

He, the warrior fierce in battle, received the

cup from Wealhtheow, and then made a speech,
630 eager for the fray. Beowulf, son of Ecgtheow,
said: —

"When I put to sea, went into the ship with
"my company of men, I purposed that I would
"once for all carry out the wish of your people,
635 "or fall in death, fast in the clutches of the foe!
"I will show the courage of a hero, or in this
"mead-hall pass my latest day!"

These words pleased the lady full well,—the
Geat's high-sounding speech. The noble queen
640 of the people, adorned with gold, went to sit by
her lord.

*(642–651) The old spirit of gladness comes back
to the men in the hall; but it is late, and Hrothgar
proposes to retire to rest.*

Then again, as of old, brave words were
spoken in the hall, the people were in gladness,
there was the clamour of a conquering warrior;
645 until at length the son of Healfdene wished to
go to his evening rest. He knew that an attack
was purposed against the high hall by the evil
spirit, from the time that they could see the sun's
light, until darkening night was over all,—
650 when shadowy shapes of darkness came stalking,
dusky beneath the clouds.

*(651–661) The company rises. Hrothgar wishes
Beowulf good fortune, entrusts Heorot to his keeping,*

G

and promises him ample recompense if his under-
taking is successful.

The whole company rose. Then the heroes
Hrothgar and Beowulf saluted each other, and
Hrothgar wished him success, power in the
banqueting-hall, and said these words: "Never
655 "yet have I entrusted the noble hall of the
"Danes to any man, since I could lift hand and
"shield, save now to thee. Take now and guard
"this best of houses, be mindful of thy fame,
"make known thy mighty valour, watch against
660 "the foe. Thou shalt lack nothing of what thou
"wilt, if thou dost escape this bold adventure
"with thy life."

X

THE WATCH FOR GRENDEL

[Lines 662–709]

(662–668) *So Hrothgar retires with his followers,
and it becomes known that he has left Heorot in
charge of a newly-appointed warden.*

Then Hrothgar, protector of the Scyldings,
departed from the hall with his band of warriors.
The war-chief wished to join Wealhtheow, his
665 queen, as consort. The King of Glory had, so
men had heard, appointed a hall-guard against
Grendel, who discharged a special office about
the lord of the Danes,—kept watch against
monsters.

(669–674) Beowulf strips himself of his armour and trusts in his sheer strength, and the favour of God.

Indeed the chief of the Geats trusted firmly
670 in his proud might, and in the favour of the
Creator. Then he took off from himself the iron
corslet, and the helmet from his head, and gave
his figured sword, choicest of weapons, to the
retainer who waited on him, and bade him guard
the war-harness!

(675–687) Boastfully does he lay stress on his intention to meet Grendel without a sword, so that there shall be a fair fight; and God shall judge.

675   Then brave Beowulf of the Geats made a
boastful speech, ere he lay down in bed: "I count
"myself no less in fighting-power, in battle-
"deeds, than Grendel does himself: and therefore
680 "by the sword I will not kill him,—rid him of
"life,—though I have the power. He knows not
"of these noble arts—to strike back at me and
"hew my shield, mighty though he be in hostile
"deeds. But we two at night shall not make use
685 "of swords, if he dare seek a combat without
"arms; and then may the wise God, the holy
"Lord, decree the triumph to whichever side
"seems meet to Him!"

(688–702) Then he and his comrades lay themselves down to sleep—the latter with little hope of ever

*seeing home again. Yet God, who rules over all, was
to give them victory over their enemies through the
might of their leader.*

Then the warrior brave in battle lay down,
the pillow received the hero's face, and around
690 him many a bold sea-warrior sank upon his
couch in hall. Not one of them supposed that
thence he would ever revisit his dear home, his
people and the noble dwelling in which he was
brought up; and they had learned that in time
695 past murderous death had taken off far too many
of the Danish people, in the wine-hall. But to
the people of the Geats, the Lord gave the
weavèd destiny of success in war,—help and
support, so that they should all overcome their
enemy through the power of one man, through
700 his own strength. It is known for certain that
God Almighty has always ruled over the race
of men.

*(702–709) In the gloom of the night came
Grendel. Beowulf alone is awake, and although it
was well known that the monster could do nothing
without the sufferance of God, he is seized by violent
emotion.*

The creature of the shadows came stalking in
the dusky night. The liegemen who had to
guard that gabled hall slept,—all except one. It
705 was well known to men that the demon foe

could not drag them to the shades below when the Creator did not will it. But he, fiercely watching for the foe, awaited in swelling rage the ordeal of battle.

XI

GRENDEL'S RAID

[Lines 710–790]

(710–724) The accursed spirit reconnoitres, bursts open the door in a rage and advances through the hall.

710   Then came Grendel, advancing from the moor under the misty slopes; God's anger rested on him. The wicked foe thought to take by treachery one of the race of men in the high hall; he strode beneath the clouds until he came to where he could very clearly discern the
715   wine-building, the gold-hall of men, gleaming with plated gold. Nor was that the first time that he had visited Hrothgar's home. Never in the days of his life, before or since, did he discover guardians in hall with worse fortune.
720   Thus the creature, deprived of joys, came journeying to the hall. The door, fastened by forged bands, fell open straightway, when he touched it with his hands. Thus, bent on destruction, for he was enraged, he tore open the door of the building.

(724–745) He revels in the thought of a feast of human flesh, and, anxiously watched by Beowulf, seizes and devours a sleeping Geat.

724   Quickly, after that, the fiend stepped on to the many-coloured paving of the floor,—advanced in angry mood; from his eyes there came a horrible light, most like a flame. He saw many men in the hall, a troop of kinsmen, a band of
730   warriors, sleeping all together. Then his spirit laughed aloud: he, the cruel monster, resolved that he would sever the life of every one of them from his body before day came; for the hope of feasting full had come to him. That was no
735   longer his fortune, that he should devour more of human kind after that night. Hygelac's mighty kinsman kept watching how the murderous foe would set to work with his sudden attacks. The monster was not minded to put it
740   off, but quickly seized a sleeping warrior as a beginning, rent him greedily, bit into his body, drank the blood from his veins, swallowed bite after bite; and soon he had eaten up all of the
745   dead man, even his feet and hands.

(745–766) Then he attacks Beowulf, who at once closes with him and holds him tight with his mighty grip. Thoroughly terrified, the monster tries to escape, but in vain!

Forward and nearer he advanced, and then

tried to seize with his hand the doughty warrior
on his bed—the fiend reached out towards him.
Beowulf at once received him with hostile intent,
750 and sat up supporting himself on his arm.
Instantly the master of crimes realized that never
in this world, these regions of earth, had he met
with a mightier hand-grip in any other man. He
became afraid in mind and spirit, but he could
get away no faster for all that. His mind was
755 bent on getting off,—he wished to flee into the
darkness and go back to the swarm of devils.
His plight was unlike anything he had met with
in his lifetime there before. Then Hygelac's
brave kinsman was mindful of what he had said
760 that evening; he stood erect and grasped him
tight, so that his fingers were strained to bursting. The monster was moving out; the chief
stepped forward too. The infamous creature
thought to slip further off, wheresoever he could,
and to flee away thence to his fen-refuge; he
knew the power of his fingers was in the foe-
765 man's grip. That was a sorry journey which that
injurious foe had made to Heorot!

(767–782) *The hall rings with their furious
struggles, and is only kept from tumbling down by
its substantial build, its extraordinary strength. The
mead-benches are wrenched from the walls; but no
one can destroy that massive building; fire alone could
consume it.*

The warrior's hall resounded, there was panic

among all the Danes, the dwellers in the stronghold, the nobles and the heroes every one. Both
770 the raging guardians of the house were furious;
the building rang again. Then was it a great
wonder that the wine-hall was proof against the
doughty fighters,—that the fair earthly dwelling
did not fall to the ground; yet it was made
775 firm enough, inside and out, by means of iron
clamps, forged with curious art. There, where
the foemen fought, many a mead-bench adorned
with gold, started from the floor, as I have
heard. Before that, wise men among the Scyld-
780 ings never thought that any man could shatter
it, splendid and horn-bedecked, in any wise, or
ruin it by craft, unless the embrace of fire should
swallow it in flame.

*(782–790) Grendel gives forth a great shriek of
despair, which strikes awe into the Danes on the
outside wall.*

A din arose, strange and mighty; a horrible
785 fear came to the North-Danes, to every one who
heard the shrieking from the wall,—heard the
adversary of God chant his grisly lay, his song
of defeat,—the prisoner of hell wailing over his
wound. He who was strongest of men in might
790 in this life's day held him fast!

XII

BEOWULF TEARS OFF GRENDEL'S ARM

[Lines 791–836]

(791–805) Still Beowulf holds him fast. His comrades come to his help with their swords, but the monster is proof against all such weapons.

The defender of nobles would not by any means let the murderous visitant escape alive,— he did not count the days of Grendel's life of use to any of the peoples. There many a noble
795 of Beowulf's company brandished an ancient ancestral weapon—they wished to protect the life of their lord, of their famous chief, if they could. They did not know, brave-minded warriors, when they took part in the contest, and
800 thought to hew at him on every side, and to hunt out his life, that no war-bill on earth, not the best of iron swords, could touch the cursèd foe, for that he used enchantment against conquering
805 weapons, every sort of blade.

(805–824) The monster's body is no help to him. The hated foe holds him fast, his arm gives way at the shoulder, the sinews part—he flees away to die, leaving his limb behind him.

In this world his parting from life was to be wretched—the alien spirit was to journey far into

the power of fiends. Then he who for long
810 before had been doing crimes, wicked in heart,
against mankind, he, the rebel against God,
discovered that his bodily frame was no help
to him, but that the bold kinsman of Hygelac
had him by the hand. While he lived, each was
815 hateful to the other. The horrible monster
suffered deadly hurt, on his shoulder gaped a
mighty wound, the sinews sprang asunder—
the tendons burst. Glory in fight was granted
to Beowulf; Grendel, sick to death, had to flee
820 thence among the fen-fastnesses—seek out his
joyless dwelling;—he knew too well that the end
of his life had come, the number of his days.
After that bloody contest, the desire of all the
Danes had come to pass!

(825–836) *Thus did Beowulf fulfil his boast, free
Heorot from its nightly terror, and end the troubles
of the Danes. As proof of victory, there was Grendel's
hand and arm and shoulder exhibited for all to
see.*

825   In such wise did he who first came from far,
the wise and brave, cleanse Hrothgar's hall and
save it from attack. He rejoiced in his night's
work, in his heroic deeds. The chief of the
Geatish men had made good his boast to the
830 East-Danes, and had removed besides all the
trouble, the sorrow wrought by malice, which
erewhile they had endured, and had to undergo

from dire compulsion,—a mighty grief. That
was clear evidence, when the brave warrior
placed under the spacious roof the hand, the
835 arm and shoulder—there was all of Grendel's
grasp complete!

XIII

THE JOY AT HEOROT

[Lines 837–924]

*(837–852) People came from far and near to see
Grendel's arm at Heorot, and rejoiced greatly. The
mere, his retreat in the neighbouring fen-country,
was dyed with blood from the doomed creature, who
took refuge in it. There he passed away and hell
received him.*

Then, in the morning, as I have heard, there
was many a warrior round the gift-hall, chiefs of
the people came from far and near along the
840 highways to see the marvel,—the traces of the
monster. His parting from life did not seem a
cause for sorrow to any of the men who saw the
trail of the inglorious one,—how he, weary in
spirit and vanquished in the fight, bore the
845 tracks of his failing life away from thence, fated
and fugitive, to the lake of the water-demons.
Then the water was boiling with blood, the
frightful surge of the waves welled up, all
mingled with hot gore,—with sword-blood; the

850 death-doomed creature had hidden himself there,
and then, deprived of joys, he gave up his life,—
his heathen soul in the fen-refuge; there hell
received him!

(853–863) *Those of Hrothgar's warriors who had
gone to the mere to see the strange sight, rode back
boldly, praising Beowulf's great feat.*

Thence the older retainers turned back, and
many a young man from the joyous journey, to
855 ride boldly from the mere on their noble steeds.
Then Beowulf's exploit was proclaimed—many
said that no other man, south or north, throughout the world, anywhere on this vast earth, was
more excellent among shield-bearers under the
860 expanse of heaven, or worthier of empire. Yet
did they not at all decry their friend and lord,
the gracious Hrothgar; he was a good king.

(864–874) *On the way they raced their horses,
and a thane of the company began to compose a lay
about Beowulf.*

Now and then the famous warriors made
865 their bay horses gallop,—run races, where the
country tracks seemed suitable,—excellent in
repute.
At times a thane of the king, a warrior filled
with poetic eloquence, who remembered many
lays, who recollected countless old traditions,

870 framed a new story in words correctly linked. The man began to set forth with skill the deed of Beowulf, and fluently to tell a well-told tale,— to weave together his words.

EPISODE OF SIGEMUND, SON OF WÆLS

(874–884) The minstrel tells of the wanderings and adventures of Sigemund, the son of Wæls, who, with his nephew Fitela, had slain many monsters. (The fact that Beowulf was also a monster-killer may have suggested the subject to the minstrel.)

874   He related almost everything that he had heard men say of Sigemund, his deeds of valour, many untold things, the struggle of the son of Wæls, his wanderings far and wide, the feuds and treacheries —things that the sons of men knew nothing of.
880   But Fitela, who had been with him, knew them, since the uncle used to tell something of such a matter to his nephew, as they had always been friends in need in every struggle, and had felled with their swords many of the race of monsters.

(884–915) Sigemund gained especial note after his death for killing with his sword a dragon, the guardian of a hoard of treasure, and taking the booty off in a ship. Heremod, a Danish king, caused much trouble to his people by his behaviour, and at last died by treachery. He is strongly contrasted with Beowulf.

884   There arose no little fame to Sigemund after his death-day, since he, hardy in battle, had killed the dragon, keeper of the hoard. Under the grey

rock, he, son of a prince, ventured the perilous
deed alone—Fitela was not with him.

890   Yet it befell him that the sword pierced through
the wondrous snake, so that it, the sterling blade,
stuck in the rock,—the dragon died a violent death.
By valour had the warrior secured that he could
895   enjoy the ring-hoard at his own will; the son of
Wæls loaded a sea-boat, bore the shining treasures
into the bosom of the ship. The dragon was consumed in its heat.

In deeds of bravery he, the protector of warriors,
900   was by far the most renowned of adventurers
among the tribes of men—he had prospered
because of that—after Heremod's warring-time had
slackened off, his might and daring. He among the
Jutes was delivered into the power of devils,
quickly slain. Too long did the surgings of sorrow
905   oppress him;—to his people, all the nobles, he was
a heavy trouble. Besides, often in times gone by,
many a wise man had bewailed the daring man's
departure, many a one who hoped from him help
out of misfortunes,—that that royal child might
910   prosper, attain his father's rank, rule over people,
citadel and treasure, the realm of heroes, the Scyldings' fatherland. Beowulf, kinsman of Hygelac,
was most beloved by all mankind and his friends;
915   but sin entered Heremod's heart.

(916–924) *Thus they journeyed home, racing from
time to time, till morning dawned. Many of them
went back to the hall to see the strange sight. Thither
did the king and queen repair also in state with a
great company of retainers.*

Once again they covered the straight roads
strewn with sand, racing, with their horses.
Then had the morning sun been quickly sent
forth. Many a retainer, valorous of mood,
went to the lofty hall to see the curious wonder;
920 the king, too, guardian of ring-hoards, came
from his bed-chamber; he, famed for noble
qualities, advanced majestically with a great
company, and his queen with him passed over
the path to the mead-hall with a retinue of
maidens.

XIV

HROTHGAR CONGRATULATES BEOWULF

[Lines 925–990]

*(925–946) Hrothgar, beholding Grendel's limb,
thanks God, who has worked so great a deliverance.
Only lately he had despaired, and his captains were
in dismay—and now a young warrior has done a
deed whereat his mother, if she still lives, may well
rejoice.*

925 Hrothgar spoke,—went to the hall, stood on
the steps, looked on the lofty roof, adorned with
gold, and Grendel's hand:—"For this sight let
"thanksgiving rise at once to the Almighty! Many
930 "horrors and afflictions have I endured through
"Grendel: yet God, the King of Glory, can ever
"work wonder on wonder. It was but now that
"I despaired of ever seeing a remedy for any of

"my troubles, since the best of houses stood
935 "stained with the blood of battle,—an all-
"embracing woe for every one of the coun-
"sellors, of those who despaired of ever guarding
"the fortress of this people from foes, from
"demons and evil spirits. Now, through the
940 "might of the Lord, a warrior has done a deed
"which up to now we all could not accomplish
"by our schemings. Lo! That self-same woman
"who bore this child among the tribes of men
945 "may say, if she still lives, that the eternal God
"has been gracious to her in her child-bearing."

(946–956) *Henceforth Hrothgar will treat him
as a son,—nothing of his which Beowulf desires
shall be denied him. His deeds shall give him everlasting fame.*

"Now, Beowulf, best of men, in my heart
"will I love thee as a son; henceforth keep well
"this new kinship. Thou shalt lack no
"earthly objects of desire of which I have con-
950 "trol. Full oft I have assigned a recompense for
"less,—honour by gifts,—and to a lesser hero,
"a weaker in the fray. Thou hast brought to
"pass for thyself by thy exploits, that thy fame
955 "shall live for ever and ever. May the Almighty
"requite thee with good, as he did but now!"

(957–979) *Beowulf answered: "Yes, I did it
"willingly and boldly. Would that thou couldst have*

"witnessed it! I meant to have killed him by my grip
"of hand, but it was not so ordained. He left his
"arm behind, but the wound is a mortal one. Soon he
"will be before the Eternal Judge."

Beowulf, son of Ecgtheow, spoke: "With right
"good will we brought that deed of daring, that
960 "onslaught, to fulfilment: perilously we adven-
"tured with mysterious powers. I heartily wish
"thou couldst thyself have seen him, the fiend
"weary unto death in his trappings. I thought
"to pin him down quickly to his death-bed by
965 "tight grips, so that he might be struggling for
"life by reason of my hand-grasp, unless his body
"had escaped. I could not keep him from going,
"—the Creator did not will it. I did not hold
"him, the deadly foe, well enough for that,—the
970 "fiend was too exceedingly strong in going.
"However, he has left behind his hand, his arm
"and shoulder to save his life and show his track.
"Yet the wretched being bought himself no
"respite thus. None the longer will the evil doer
975 "live, tortured by sins; but pain has seized him
"tightly in its forceful grip, with deadly bonds.
"Thus shall the creature stained with crime wait
"for the Last Judgment;—how the glorious
"Creator will sentence him!"

(980–990) *Unferth, the son of Ecglaf, is the
less boastful after all the nobles have seen for themselves the hand, the sword-proof claws of the monster.*

980   Then was the son of Ecglaf a man more spar-
ing of his boastful talk concerning warlike deeds,
after the nobles had, through the chief's prowess,
looked on the hand above the lofty roof, on the
985 fingers of the foe. The tip of each one, each place
of the nails, of the heathen warrior's hateful
and horrible claw, was most like steel. Every-
one said that there was no hard thing which
could bite into him, no well-proved sword which
990 would sever the bloody fighting-limb of the
demon.

XV

THE BANQUET AND THE GIFTS

[Lines 991–1049]

*(991–1002) Heorot was decorated by willing hands
for a banquet, although much shattered by the fiend
in his efforts to escape.*

Forthwith it was ordered that Heorot should
be adorned within by men's hands. Many there
were of men and women who prepared that
festive hall, that habitation for retainers. The
995 tapestries shone gold-embroidered along the
walls, many wondrous sights for those among
men who gaze upon such things. That radiant
house, all bound within with iron bands, had
been greatly shattered; the door-hinges were
broken: the roof alone had kept entirely sound,

1000 when the demon, stained with guilty deeds, turned and fled, despairing of life.

(1002–1008) Death is not easy to escape from, —a man must go when he is fated.

That is not easy to escape from, let him try it who will; but a man must seek that place pre- pared for those who have souls, earth-dwelling 1005 sons of men, forced on by fate, when his body, fast in its bed of rest, shall sleep after the banquet of this life.

(1008–1019) Hrothgar went himself to the feast, which was attended by a great and joyous company. There was much drinking of mead, and there was no sign of the treachery which was to come in later times.

Then it was due time that Healfdene's son should go into the hall; the king himself would 1010 take part in the banquet. Never have I heard that people bore themselves better round their treasure-giver, in a greater company. The men of great renown there seated themselves upon the benches, rejoiced in feasting, courteously 1015 drank many a cup of mead; Hrothgar and Hrothulf, the mighty kinsmen, were in the high hall. Heorot was filled within with friends, —not yet then had the Scyldings people used treachery.

(1020–1034)   Costly presents were bestowed on Beowulf by the king—a banner, a corslet, a helmet and a jewelled sword of honour.

1020   Then the son of Healfdene bestowed on Beowulf as the meed of victory a gilded ensign, a decorated battle-banner, a helmet and a corslet; many saw the jewelled sword of honour borne before the hero. Beowulf drank
1025 of the cup in hall; no need had he to be ashamed of the costly gifts before the warriors. Not many men have I known to give more heartily four such treasures, decked with gold, to others on the ale-bench.

1030   Around the helmet's crown, a projecting rim surrounded with bands, guarded the head above, that the sword wrought by files, hard in the storm of battle, might not sorely injure it, when the shielded warrior must go forth against foes.

(1035–1042)   Besides these were eight horses caparisoned with gold, one being Hrothgar's own charger and bearing a curious saddle.

1035   Then the protector of nobles bade eight horses with gold-plated bridles, be brought into the hall, within the building. On one of them was placed a saddle cunningly inlaid, adorned with jewels,—that was the war-seat of the mighty
1040 king, when Healfdene's son wished to take part in the play of swords. Never did courage fail

the far-famed chieftain at the front, when men were falling dead.

(*1043–1049*) *No one could say that Hrothgar was niggardly with his gifts.*

And then the lord of Ing's descendants, the 1045 Danes, gave Beowulf ownership of both the two, of horses and of weapons,—bade him enjoy them well. In such manly wise did the renowned prince, treasure-warden of heroes, repay Beowulf for his battle-rushes with horses and with treasures, so that never man who wills to speak the truth in fairness shall disparage them.

XVI AND XVII

THE SONG OF HROTHGAR'S MINSTREL. THE LAY OF
HNÆF AND HENGEST

[Lines 1050–1191]

(*1050–1062*) *In addition, Hrothgar bestows meet rewards on each of Beowulf's company, and makes amends with gold for the loss of the man whom Grendel devoured. The poet moralizes.*

1050 Besides that, the chief of the nobles bestowed something precious, an heirloom, at the mead-bench, on each one of those who had traversed the ocean-way with Beowulf ; and he bade recompense be made with gold for that one whom

1055 Grendel had lately killed in his wickedness,—as
he would have done more of them, had not all-
seeing God and the courage of the man kept off
that fate. The Creator guided all the race of men,
as he still does now. Wherefore understanding,
1060 forethought of mind, is best in every way. Much
shall he experience of good and evil, who here,
in these troublous times, long makes the earth
his dwelling-place.

*(1063–1070)   Hrothgar's bard sings a lay to the
sound of the harp.*

There was singing and music together in
accompaniment in presence of Healfdene's war-
1065 like chieftain; the harp was played, and many
a lay rehearsed, when Hrothgar's bard was to
provide entertainment in hall along the mead-
bench,—about the sons of Finn, and how disaster came on them, and how Hnæf, hero of
the Half-Danes, of the Scyldings, fell in deadly
fight against the Frisians.

EPISODE OF KING FINN

[Lines 1071–1159]

*This part of the poem is very obscure, and is rather
a string of allusions than a narrative. At any rate
it presupposes a knowledge on the part of the hearer
of facts which are not set out in the lay.*

*As far as the episode in Beowulf goes, the story
appears to be briefly thus:—*

Finn, king of the Frisians and son of Folcwalda, marries Hildeburh, sister of Hnæf, and daughter of Hoc, a Scylding chieftain.

Hnæf is staying with his sister Hildeburh when a quarrel arises and Hnæf is slain in a night attack (described in the Finnesburg Fragment) on the hall in which he and his followers are lodging. A son of Hildeburh is also slain.

After that there is a treaty of peace, which provides that as winter is coming on, Hengest, who may have been Hnæf's chief man (of the Jutes) and his followers (a mixed band counting many Danes), shall be allowed to remain in the Frisian country and be treated by the king (Finn) on equal terms with his own subjects. Hengest, however, broods over the past, and plans revenge after the winter is over, being incited thereto by Hunlafing or 'son of Hunlaf.' In the spring the Danes Guthlaf and Oslaf (one of whom is possibly actually the Hunlafing of the poem) sail back to Denmark, and collect a picked band, return to Friesland where Hengest is probably awaiting them and the combined forces, kill Finn in his own castle, and take Queen Hildeburh back to Denmark.

1071

"Hildburh, truly, had no cause to praise the "good faith of the Jutes; without offence she "was deprived of her dear ones at the shield-"play, her son and brother; wounded by the
1075 "spear, they fell as was fated; a sad princess "was she! Not by any means did the daughter of "Hoc mourn without reason over the decree of fate, "when morning came—when she could see in the "light of day the slaughter of her kinsfolk where

"she once possessed the highest earthly pleasure.

1080 "Warfare had taken off all Finn's retainers save only
"a few, so that he might not in any way fight to
"a finish the fight against Hengest, the prince's
"general, at that meeting-place, nor dislodge the
"sad survivors by fighting; but Hengest and his

1085 "men offered them terms, that they must give up
"to them entirely another hall, a chamber and
"a seat of honour, that they might share equal
"possession of it with the sons of the Jutes, and that
"at the giving of treasure the son of Folcwalda

1090 "(Finn) would each day honour the Danes,—would
"gratify with rings the troop of Hengest, even
"with just so much costly treasure of plated gold
"as he would cheer the Frisian race with in the
"banqueting-hall.

1095 "Then on both sides they ratified a treaty of
"fast friendship. Finn declared to Hengest with
"oaths, absolutely and unreservedly, that he would
"treat the sad survivors honourably according to
"the ordinance of his counsellors, that no man

1100 "there should break the covenant by word or deed,
"nor mention it by malicious artifice, although they
"would be following the slayer of their generous
"prince, being without a lord—for it was forced
"upon them thus; and if any of the Frisians should

1105 "call to mind the blood-feud by provoking words,
"then the edge of the sword should settle it. The
"funeral pyre was made ready, and gleaming gold
"was brought up from the hoard.

"The best of the War-Scyldings, the battle-
"heroes, was ready on the funeral pile. At the

1110 "pyre the blood-stained corslet, the swine-image

"all-golden, the boar hard as iron, and many a
"noble killed by wounds, were visible to all.
"Mighty men had fallen in the carnage. Then
"Hildeburh ordered her own son to be given over to
1115 "the flames at Hnæf's funeral pile—his body to be
"burned and put upon the pyre at his uncle's side.
"The unhappy woman mourned, and lamented in
"dirges. The war-hero ascended the pyre. The
"greatest of funeral fires curled upwards to the
1120 "clouds, roared before the grave-mound; heads
"were consumed, gashes gaped open : then the blood
"sprang forth from the body, where the foe had
"wounded it. The fire, greediest of spirits, had
"consumed all of those whom war had carried off,
"of either people—their glory had passed away."

[XVII]

1125 "Then the warriors, deprived of their friends,
"went off to visit their dwellings, to see the Frisian
"land, their homes and high stronghold. Hengest
"still, however, stayed through that slaughter-
"stained winter with Finn, very unhappily; his native
"land was in his thoughts, albeit he might not guide
1130 "over the sea a ship with curved prow. The ocean
"heaved with storm, contended with the wind;
"winter had locked the waves in its icy bond, until
"a new spring came round to the homes of men,
"and the seasons gloriously bright, regularly
1135 "observing their order, as they still do now."

"Then the winter was past, the bosom of
"earth was fair, the exiled guest was anxious to
"depart from the dwellings, yet he (Hengest)
"thought rather about vengeance than a sea-

1140 "voyage, whether he could not bring about a
"hostile encounter, because he would remember
"with his sword the sons of the Jutes. Hence he did
"not refuse battle to the leader of the host (Finn)
"when the son of Hunlaf placed on his lap Hilde-
"leoma, best of swords. Its edges were well known
1145 "among the giants. Moreover, cruel death by the
"sword afterwards befell the daring-minded Finn at
"his own home, when Guthlaf and Oslaf made sad
"complaint, after their sea-voyage, about the fierce
"attack,—blamed him for their share of woes.
1150 "The troubled spirit (of strife) in their breasts could
"no longer be repressed.

"Then was the hall reddened with corpses of
"the foes; Finn, the king, likewise was slain among
"his guard, and the queen taken. The warriors of
"the Scyldings bore to the ship all the possessions
1155 "of the country's king,—whatsoever they could
"find at Finn's homestead of necklaces and curious
"gems. They brought the noble lady over the sea-
"path to the Danes, and led her to her people."

*(1159–1162) After the lay is ended, the rejoicings
proceed.*

1159 The song, the gleeman's lay was sung.
Then mirth rose high, the noise of revelry was
clearly heard; cup-bearers proffered wine from
curious vessels.

*(1162–1174) Queen Wealhtheow, wearing her
crown, approaches the kingly throne, where Hrothgar
and his nephew Hrothulf are sitting, with Unferth*

at the King's feet. At that time the relations between
uncle and nephew were cordial. She hands the cup
to Hrothgar, and bids him be of good cheer and
gracious to the Geats.

Then Wealhtheow came forth, and went,
wearing a golden diadem, to where the two
nobles sat, uncle and nephew ; peace was between
1165 them still, each to the other true. Moreover,
there sat Unferth the spokesman at the Scylding chieftain's feet ; all of them trusted in his
spirit, that he had much courage, although he
might not have been upright with his kinsfolk
at the play of swords.

Then spake the Queen of the Scyldings : —
"Take this cup, my noble lord, giver of treasure.
1170 "Be thou of joyous mood, free-handed friend of
"men, and speak to the Geats with kindly words :
"for so one ought to do. Be gracious towards
"the Geats, mindful of gifts, which thou hast
"from far and near."

(1175-1187) Hearing that Hrothgar purposes
to adopt Beowulf as a son, she discreetly suggests
to the king to be generous to him, but to leave the
kingdom to his own descendants. If he dies soon, she
feels sure that Hrothulf will prove a faithful guardian
to his children (Hrethric and Hrothmund), knowing
what kindness he has received from the king and
herself.

1175 "It has been said to me that thou wouldst have

"this warrior as a son. The radiant ring-hall
"Heorot is cleansed. Dispense, while thou mayst,
"many gifts; and leave the people and the realm
"to thy descendants, when thou shalt pass away
1180 "to meet thy appointed fate. I know my gracious
"Hrothulf, that he will honourably entreat our
"children, if thou, lord of the Scyldings, leavest
"the world sooner than he. I trust that he will
1185 "faithfully requite our sons, if he is mindful of
"all the honour which in the past we both con-
"ferred on him for his pleasure and advance-
"ment while he was yet a child."

*(1188–1191) Then she goes to where her sons
are sitting with Beowulf and the younger men at
arms.*

Then she turned to the bench where her boys
were,—Hrethric and Hrothmund,—and the
1190 sons of the heroes, the younger warriors together, where the brave Beowulf of the Geats
sat by the two brothers.

XVIII

BEOWULF HONOURED WITH GIFTS

THE HEROES REST

[Lines 1192–1250]

*(1192–1201) The cup is borne to Beowulf and
he is further loaded with costly presents—gold and*

jewels—and notably a circlet is given him than which there was none better save the necklace of the Brisings, which Hama carried off when he fled from Eormenric.

To him the cup was borne, and friendly invitation was offered in words, and twisted gold
1195 graciously presented: two armlets, a mantle and rings, and the finest of torques that I have ever known of in this world. Never under heaven have I heard of any better hoarded gem of heroes since Hama carried off to the glorious fortress the necklace of the Brisings, the orna-
1200 ment in its costly setting,—he fled the snares of Eormenric and chose lasting gain.

(1202–1214) The subsequent history of the collar given to Beowulf follows,—how Hygelac, king of the Geats, wore it on his last rash and fatal expedition against the Frisians, and it passed into their possession.

That circlet had Hygelac the Geat, the grand-son of Swerting, on his last exploit, when under his banner he defended his treasure,—guarded
1205 the spoil of battle. Fate took him off when from reckless daring he brought trouble on himself, feud with the Frisians. He, the mighty chieftain, had borne the jewels, the precious stones, across the cup of the waves; he died beneath his shield. Then the body of the king

1210 passed into the power of the Franks,—breast-
armour and torque as well; less worthy warriors
plundered the slain after the battle; people of
the Geats remained in that place of corpses.

*(1215–1231) Wealhtheow wishes him luck of his
circlet and mantle, and commends her boys to him.
With her good wishes she mingles wise advice.*

1215   The hall was filled with the noise of applause.
Wealhtheow spoke; she said before the company:
"In prosperity enjoy this circlet, Beowulf, be-
"loved youth, and this mantle—state-treasures
"—and thrive well! Be known for valour, and be
1220 "kind in counsel to these boys. For that will I be
"mindful of largess towards thee! Thou hast
"brought it to pass that men will magnify thee
"far and near, to all eternity, even as widely as
"the sea, the home of the winds, surrounds the
1225 "cliffs. Be prosperous, prince, so long as thou
" dost live. I wish thee store of costly treasures.
"Be friendly to my son in deeds, thou blessed
"one! Here is each noble true to other, in spirit
"mild, and faithful to his lord. The retainers
1230 "are well disposed, the people all alert, the
"warriors have drunk deep; they do my bidding."

*(1232–1250) After the choice banquet was over,
Hrothgar went away to his room, and the hall was
cleared for sleeping. At each man's head lay his
armour, as was the custom, so that they might be
ready for night-attacks or surprises.*

Then she went to her seat. There was the
finest of banquets; men drank wine; they knew
not fate, grim destiny, as it had gone forth for
1235 many of the nobles.

When even had come and Hrothgar had departed to his dwelling,—the chieftain to his rest,
unnumbered nobles watched over the hall,
as they had often done before. They cleared the
bench-boards, and it was spread about with
1240 beds and bolsters. Among the feasters one sank
on his hall-bed ready for death and doomed.
They set war-bucklers at their heads, the shining
shield-wood. There on the bench, above each
1245 noble, was exposed the helmet, prominent in
war, the corslet of linked mail, the proud spear-
shaft. It was their practice to be ever ready for
the fray at home and in the field, and in either
1250 case at just such times as need befell their lord.
They were a doughty race!

B.—*BEOWULF AND GRENDEL'S MOTHER*
XIX

[Lines 1251–1320]

(1251–1254)   Thus they went to sleep—a sleep which cost one of them his life!

AND so they fell asleep. One paid a heavy price for his night's rest, as had befallen them full oft since Grendel had inhabited the gold-hall,—practised wrong, until the end came—death after his crimes.

(1255–1276)   There was a widespread rumour that another monster still lived, of whom Grendel was the offspring. This creature brooded over the loss of Grendel, whose origin (from Cain, cp. l. 111) is again referred to, as well as his defeat by Beowulf.

1255   It became manifest,—widely known to men,
—that an avenger still lived after the hateful
foe—a long time after the troublous strife.
Grendel's mother, monstrous among women-
kind, brooded over her misery—she who must
1260 needs inhabit the dread waters, chilling streams,
after Cain slew by the sword his one brother,

—his father's son. Cain then had gone forth out-
lawed, branded for murder, to flee the joys of
1265 men,—lodged in the wilderness. From him were
born numbers of fateful spirits, of whom Grendel
was one, a hateful outcast-foe, who at Heorot
had found a watchful mortal waiting for the fray.
The monster there had laid hold of him; yet he
1270 bore in mind the power of his might, the lavish
gift which God had granted him, and trusted
himself to the Lord for grace, help and support.
Hence he had overcome the foe, struck down the
demon of hell. Then he, the enemy of mankind,
1275 had gone off, abased, deprived of joy, to see his
house of death.

*(1276–1280) Grendel's mother resolves to go to
Heorot and avenge his death.*

And his mother, ravenous and gloomy,
resolved in spite of it to go a sorry journey and
avenge the death of her son. So she came to
1280 Heorot, where the Ring-Danes slept about the
hall.

*(1280–1287) Terror again seized the dwellers
in the hall, though less than in Grendel's case, as
might have been expected when a woman was in
question.*

Then forthwith there came a reverse for the
nobles, when Grendel's mother entered within.

I

The fear was less by just so much as women's
strength, a woman's war-terror, is, as compared
1285 with that caused by a man, when the orna-
mented, hammer-forged blade, the blood-stained
sword, trusty of edge, cleaves through the boar-
image on the helmet of the foe.

(1288–1291) *The warriors hurriedly seize their
swords—there was no time to put on armour.*

Then in the hall, from above the benches, the
hard-edged sword was taken down; many a
1290 broad shield was raised, firm in the hand.
When the terror seized him, none thought of
helm or great corslet.

(1292–1301) *The monster snatched up one of
the men—Æschere, a high favourite of Hrothgar—
and made off with him to the fens. Beowulf was
not there; another sleeping-place had been assigned
to him.*

She was in haste,—wished to be off from
thence to save her life, when she had been dis-
1295 covered. Quickly she grasped firmly one of the
nobles, and then she went towards the fen. He
was to Hrothgar most beloved of champions between the seas of those of the rank of retainer, a
mighty shield-warrior, a well-known hero, whom
she killed in his resting-place.
1300   Beowulf was not there, but before that, after

the giving of treasure, another lodging-place had been allotted to the noble Geat.

(1302–1309) A wail of anguish goes up from Heorot, and Hrothgar is again overwhelmed with grief.

There was clamour in Heorot. She took the well-known hand covered with blood; sorrow was renewed—had come again to the building. 1305 That was no good exchange—that they should pay on both sides with the lives of loved ones.

Then the aged king, the hoary warrior, was sad at heart, after he knew his dearest counsellor was dead,—deprived of life.

(1310–1320) Beowulf is hastily summoned to a council, and goes to the king's chamber with his company. He asks whether the king has had a good night.

1310 Quickly was Beowulf, victory-blest hero, summoned to the King's chamber. With break of day the princely champion went amongst his nobles, himself with his comrades, where the wise king waited, if haply the Almighty would 1315 ever bring about a change for him, after the spell of woe.

Then the man distinguished in battle walked across the floor with his little band,—the hall-timbers resounded—that he might greet with

words the wise lord of the children of Ing—
1320 ask if the night had been peaceful according to
his wish.

XX

HROTHGAR LAMENTS THE LOSS OF ÆSCHERE, AND
DESCRIBES THE HAUNT OF GRENDEL'S MOTHER

[Lines 1321–1382]

*(1321–1344) The king tells Beowulf of the
death of his dear friend Æschere, (whom he praises
highly) and explains in what sort it fell out. This is
evidently a piece of revenge on the part of Grendel's
mother.*

Hrothgar, the Scyldings' protector, replied:
"Ask not thou after joy! Sorrow is come anew
"to the people of the Danes! Æschere is dead,
1325 "Yrmenlaf's elder brother, my trusted coun-
"sellor, my adviser and comrade, when we in
"battle defended our heads, when foot-men
"fought, and hewed at boar-crests. Æschere was
"such a man as a noble should be, a chieftain
1330 "most excellent. The wandering demon has slain
"him in Heorot. I know not whither the terrible
"creature returned—proud of her carrion, made
"glad by her feasting. She has avenged the
"quarrel,—that thou last night didst kill Grendel
1335 "in fierce fashion by tight grips, because he had
"too long reduced and killed my people. He fell
"in battle, forfeit of his life. And now another

"mighty miscreant has come, and would avenge
1340 "her son; and she has carried the feud far, as it
"may seem to many a thane who mourns his
"treasure-giver in his heart—a heavy sorrow.
"Now does the hand lie dead which helped your
"almost every desire."

*(1345–1376) Hrothgar, too, had heard that there
were two monsters—one a female,—and in a graphic
passage he describes their haunt, a gloomy mere not
far distant, over which a sort of will-o'-the-wisp hovers
at night. Rather than plunge into it, the hart chased
by hounds will die on the bank.*

1345   "I have heard dwellers in the country, subjects
"of mine, counsellors in hall, say this:—that
"they have seen two such huge wanderers of the
"marches guarding the moors, alien spirits, of
"whom one was, so far as they could most
1350 "clearly tell, the semblance of a woman. The
"other wretched one whom, in past days,
"dwellers in the land named Grendel, trod exile-
"paths in human form, howbeit he was greater
"than any other man. They have no knowledge
1355 "of a father, whether any such had been begot-
"ten for them in times past among the mysterious
"demons. They dwell in a land unknown, wolf-
"haunted slopes, wind-swept headlands, perilous
"marsh-paths, where the mountain stream goes
1360 "down under the mists of the cliffs,—a flood
"under the earth. It is not far hence, in miles,

"that the lake stands over which hang groves
"covered with frost: the wood, firm-rooted, over-
"shadows the water.

1365   "There may be seen each night a fearful won-
"der,—fire on the flood! Of the sons of men
"none lives so wise as to know the bottom. Al-
"though, pressed by the hounds, the ranger of
"the heath, the hart strong in its horns, may seek
1370 "the forest, chased from far, he will give up his
"life, his being, on the brink, sooner than he
"will plunge in it to save his head. That is no
"pleasant spot. Thence rises up the surging
"water darkly to the clouds, when the wind stirs
1375 "up baleful storms, until the air grows misty, the
"heavens weep."

(*1376–1382*) *Now again does Hrothgar appeal
to Beowulf for help. If he will seek out the monster
rich rewards shall be his.*

"Now once more is help to be had from thee
"alone. Thou knowest not yet the haunt, the
"perilous place, where thou mayest find the sin-
"stained being. Seek it if thou darest! I will
1380 " reward thee for the struggle with riches, with
"ancient treasures, as I did before,—with twisted
"gold, if thou dost escape."

XXI

THE EXPEDITION TO THE MERE

[Lines 1383–1472]

(1383–1389) Beowulf bids Hrothgar be of good cheer. Since we must all die, the best thing is to win a reputation while we may.

Beowulf, son of Ecgtheow, answered: "Sor-"row not, wise man. Better is it for each one of
1385 "us that he should avenge his friend, than greatly "mourn. Each of us must expect an end of living "in this world; let him who may win glory "before death: for that is best at last for the "departed warrior."

(1390–1398) He will go to work at once, and he promises Hrothgar that the monster shall not escape.

1390 "Rise, guardian of the realm! Come, let us "go at once, and spy the track of Grendel's "kinswoman. I promise thee she shall not escape "to cover, neither to the lap of earth, nor into "mountain wood, nor to the ocean's depth,
1395 "go where she may! This day do thou have "patience in all thy woes, as I expect of thee!"

(1399–1417) Hrothgar thanks God, takes horse, and tracks the footprints of the weird creature. Beowulf himself, with a handful of followers, goes

forward through difficult country till he reaches a gloomy lake.

Then the veteran sprang up,—thanked God, the mighty Lord, for what the man had said.
1400 Then was a horse bridled for Hrothgar, a steed with plaited mane. The wise prince advanced in stately manner: the foot-force of shield-bearers went forth. Along the forest-paths footprints were freely visible—her course over the lands.
1405 She had gone forth over the dusky moors, and borne lifeless the best of vassals of those who watched over the home with Hrothgar. Then the sons of nobles went over the steep, rocky slopes, the narrow ways, the thin, lone paths
1410 —an unknown course,—the beetling crags, many homes of water-monsters. He with a few skilled men went on before to view the place: till suddenly he found mountain trees hanging
1415 over a grey rock—a dismal wood. The water was below, blood-stained and turbid.

(1418–1423) There a ghastly sight meets the whole company. Æschere's head is found on a cliff, beside the blood-stained waters.

It was a grievous thing at heart for all the Danes, the Scyldings' friends, for many a chief-
1420 tain to suffer,—pain for each of the nobles, when they found Æschere's head upon the lake cliff. The water surged with blood, with hot gore: the people gazed on it.

*(1423–1432) The troop sit down, watch the water-
monsters in and about the lake, and scare them by the
sound of their war-horn.*

At times the horn sang out an eager battle-
note. The warriors all sat down. Then they
1425 beheld about the water many of the race of
reptiles, wondrous sea-dragons exploring the
deep. Upon the cliff-slopes, too, they saw sea-
monsters lie, like those who at morning-time
take their disaster-bringing course over the sail-
road, serpents and savage beasts. They rushed
1430 away, bitter and enraged,—they had heard the
noise, the war-horn's note.

*(1432–1441) One of them is shot by an arrow
from Beowulf's bow, despatched by boar-spears and
hauled on to the cliff, a marvel to the onlookers.*

One the chief of the Geats severed from
life, from his battling with the waters, by his
shafted bow, so that the hard war-arrow stuck in
1435 his vitals:—he was the slower at swimming in
the mere, for that death had carried him off.
Quickly he was hard pressed upon the waves
with sharp-barbed boar-spears,—subdued by
force and dragged on to the cliff, a wondrous
1440 offspring of the waves. Men examined the
horrible enemy.

(1441–1472) Beowulf dons his armour, his trusty

war-corslet and wondrous helmet; he takes also
Hrunting, a famous sword which Unferth lends
him, and prepares to plunge into the lake. Unferth
himself, for all his boasting, dares not risk his life
therein.

Beowulf arrayed himself with princely armour; no whit did he feel anxious for his life.
His war-corslet, woven by hand, ample and
1445 deftly worked, was to make trial of the mere. It
had power to shield his body, so that for him
the battle-grasp, the fury's vengeful grip, might
do no damage to his breast, his life! The shining
helmet screened his head, which was to stir up
1450 the watery depths, to tempt the churning waves.
It was adorned with gold, encircled with lordly
bands, as in past days the weapon-smith had
wrought it,—formed it wondrously, and set it
round with boar-images, so that after that no
1455 sword or battle-knife could ever cut through it.
That, too, was not the least of mighty aids, which
Hrothgar's spokesman lent him in his need.
Hrunting was the name of that hilted sword,
which was one among the foremost of ancient
heirlooms. The blade was iron, patterned by
1460 twigs of venom, hardened with blood of battle.
Never had it failed any man in time of war, of
those who grasped it with their hands, who dared
enter upon perilous adventures, the meeting-
place of foes:—not the first time was that, that
1465 it had bold work to do. When he lent the weapon

to a braver swordsman, surely the son of Ecglaf,
lusty in strength, did not remember what he had
said before, when drunk with wine. Himself he
dared not risk his life beneath the tumult of the
waves,—accomplish deeds of prowess. There
1470 he lost his fame,—renown for valour. Not thus
was it with that other, when he had made ready
for the fray.

XXII

BEOWULF'S PARTING WORDS. HE ATTACKS
THE MONSTER

[Lines 1473–1556]

(*1473–1491*) *Then, in case he loses his life,
Beowulf reminds Hrothgar of his promises. He
pledges him to protect his trusty followers, and to
hand over to Hygelac the presents he had given him.
The latter will see what a generous rewarder Beowulf
had! He also enjoins Hrothgar to hand back to
Unferth the sword Hrunting, with which he means
to conquer or die!*

Beowulf, son of Ecgtheow, spoke: "Remem-
"ber now, O famous son of Healfdene, wise
1475 "chief, generous friend of men, now that I am
"ready to start, what we two said a while ago:—
"if I for thy necessity should cease from life,
"that thou wouldst always be in a father's place
1480 "to me when I am gone. Be thou a guardian of
"my retainers, my close companions, if combat

"takes me off; and send thou also to Hygelac
"the treasures which thou gavest me, beloved
"Hrothgar. The Geatish lord may then per-
1485 "ceive from the gold,—the son of Hrethel see,
"when he looks on the treasure, that I have
"found out a good ring-giver, high in excel-
"lence,—enjoyed his bounty while I might.

"And let thou Unferth, widely famous man,
"have the ancient heirloom, the curious sword
1490 "with a wavy pattern, hard of its edge. I will
"with Hrunting gain renown, or death shall
"take me off!"

*(1492–1500) Then he goes down into the lake, and
it is a good part of the day before he gets to the
bottom. Grendel's mother becomes aware that her
retreat is being invaded.*

After these words the chief of the Geats
pressed bravely on, and would not even wait an
answer. The surging water received the warrior.
1495 It was a good part of the day before he could
descry the solid bottom. Quickly she who,
fiercely ravenous, had ranged the watery realm
for fifty years, greedy and grim, found that one
1500 of the human kind was there, examining from
above the home of monsters.

*(1501–1505) She clutches at him, but his goodly
harness protects him, and he comes to no hurt.*

Then she clutched at him, she seized the

warrior with her horrid claws; for all that, she
did not so soon wound his unharmed frame:—
outside the ring-mail hedged him round, so that
she could not break the corslet through, the
1505 linked mail-shirt, with her hateful fingers.

*(1506–1512) Howbeit she drags him downwards
to her lair, and he is much hindered in using his
weapons, and in swimming, by the clasp of his adversary and the attacks of other water-sprites.*

Then the she-wolf of the water, when she
came to the bottom, bore the ring-clad lord to
her own dwelling, so that, however brave he was,
he could not wield his weapons; for so many of
1510 the weird creatures hampered him in swimming.
Many a sea-beast tried to break through his shirt
of mail with its warlike tusks,—the monsters
pursued him.

*(1512–1528) At last he comes to a cavern to which
the water has no access, and by the lurid flame therein
he descries the mere-wife and deals her a desperate
blow with his sword. But for the first time the
weapon fails—it glances back from the head of the
monster.*

Then the chief perceived that he was in some
unfriendly hall or other, where no water harmed
1515 him in any way, nor might the sudden rush of
the flood touch him, by reason of the vaulted

chamber;—a fiery light he saw, a glaring flame
shine brightly. Then the brave man perceived
the accursed monster of the deep, the mighty
mere-wife. He gave a forceful impulse to his
1520 battle-sword; his hand did not hold back the
blow,—so that the patterned blade sang out a
greedy war-song on her head. Then the stranger
found that the shining weapon would not bite,
could do no harm to life; but the blade failed the
1525 chieftain in his need. It had stood many close
encounters in times past, had often cleft the
helmet, the corslet of the doomed; that was
the first time for the precious treasure that its
glory failed.

(*1529–1536*) *Nothing daunted, Beowulf flings
aside the sword and trusts to his mighty hand-grip.*

Hygelac's kinsman was still resolute: by no
1530 means slack in courage, bent on daring deeds.
Then the furious fighter cast aside the damasked
sword, covered with ornament, so that it lay on
the ground, rigid and steely-edged; he trusted
to his strength, the hand-grip of his might. So
1535 must a man do when he thinks to win enduring
fame in war—he will have no care about his life.

(*1537–1556*) *He seizes the monster by the shoulder
and flings her to the ground; but he stumbles
and she gets upon him, and draws her dagger. She
cannot, however, pierce his armour—God and his
war-corslet protect him, and he stands upright once
more.*

The prince of the War-Geats then seized Grendel's mother by the shoulder—he grieved not at the struggle;—the brave in combat, burst-ing as he was with rage, so flung the deadly
1540 foe that she fell upon the ground. She quickly yielded him a recompense again with fearful graspings, and clutched at him. Sick at heart, the strongest of warriors, of foot-combatants, stumbled so that he had a fall.

1545 She threw herself then on her hall-visitant and drew her dagger, broad and bright of edge;— she would avenge her child, her only offspring. The woven hauberk lay upon his shoulder. That preserved his life, barred entry against point and
1550 edge. Then the son of Ecgtheow, the hero of the Geats, would have perished under the wide earth, had not his war-corslet, his strong coat of mail, furnished him succour, and the holy God, the all-wise Lord, brought about victory
1555 in battle. With ease, the Ruler of the heavens decided it aright after Beowulf had got up again.

XXIII

END OF THE FIGHT WITH GRENDEL'S MOTHER

THE RETURN

[Lines 1557–1650]

(1557–1572) *At this time Beowulf sees in the vault an ancient giant-made sword, seizes it, and with*

the courage of despair, deals the monster a fearful
blow in the neck, whereat she falls and dies, and a
new brightness fills the chamber.

He saw then among the armour a victory-blest
weapon, an ancient giant-made sword, doughty
1560 of edge, the glory of warriors; choicest of
weapons that; howbeit it was greater than any
other man could carry to the battle-play, good
and majestical, the work of giants. Then he,
champion of the Scyldings, seized the orna-
1565 mented hilt; swung the patterned blade, savage
and fierce in battle; struck furiously, reckless of
life, so that the sword smote her sharply on the
neck and broke the bones. The blade cleft her
doomed body through and through; on the floor
1570 she fell. The sword was gory, the man rejoiced
in his work. A gleam flashed forth, light was
diffused within, as when the candle of the firmament shines brightly from heaven.

(1572–1590) Then Beowulf examines the vault,
sword in hand, and lights upon the carcass of Grendel,
whose head he cuts off.

He gazed about the chamber and then turned
along the wall; Hygelac's thane, incensed and
resolute, raised the weapon firmly by the hilt.
1575 The blade was not useless to the hero: for he
wished at once to pay back Grendel for the many
raids which he had made upon the West-Danes,
far oftener than at that one time when he slew

1580 Hrothgar's hearth-companions in their slumber,
—ate fifteen men of Danish race while sleeping,
and bore off as many more, a hateful booty. He,
wrathful warrior, had given him his reward for
1585 that, so that he now saw Grendel lying in his
resting-place, worn out with fighting, destitute
of life, as he had been maimed erewhile in fight at
Heorot. The body gaped wide when it met the
blow, the lusty sword-stroke after death; and
1590 Beowulf cut off his head.

(1591–1605) *The onlookers on the bank of the
mere now observe that its waters are troubled and
stained with blood; they give way to gloomy forebodings, and at three o'clock in the afternoon Hrothgar and his Danes return home, leaving Beowulf's
little band of followers still faithfully waiting for their
lord, but almost in despair.*

As soon as the clear-sighted followers who
looked upon the mere with Hrothgar noticed
that the surging water was all churned up, the
lake stained with blood, the grey-haired
1595 veterans spoke together about the hero,
saying that they did not expect the noble
chief again—that he would come rejoicing
in victory, to seek their famous prince; for it
seemed to many that the sea-wolf had destroyed
him.
1600 Then came the ninth hour of the day; the brave
Scyldings quitted the headland; the generous

friend of men returned home from thence.

The strangers sat down, sick at heart, and gazed upon the mere; they wished, but did not expect that they should see their friend and 1605 lord again.

(1605–1617) Beowulf takes but little spoil in the cave—Grendel's head and the hilt of the sword—for the blade had been dissolved by the poisonous blood of the monster.

Then the sword, the war-blade, began to waste away in gory fragments like icicles, by reason of the foeman's blood. It was a great marvel that it all melted, very like to ice, when the 1610 Father—he who has mastery of times and seasons,—loosens the bond of frost, unwinds the flood-ropes. He is the true Lord.

He, prince of the Geats, did not take more of precious objects in the caves,—though he saw many there,—than the head, and the hilt besides, 1615 adorned with treasure. The sword was already melted, the damasked blade burnt up,—so hot had been the blood, the fiend so poisonous, who had died in that place.

(1618–1628) Soon he is swimming upwards again through the now purified waters, and lands amid the rejoicings of his company.

Soon he was swimming who had in the fray

survived the onslaught of the foes; he swam
1620 upwards through the water; the swirling eddies,
the broad expanses were all purged, when the
alien spirit gave up the days of his life and this
transitory world. Then came to land the sea-
men's chief, boldly swimming, and revelled in
1625 his lake-booty, the mighty burden of those things
which he had with him. Then the splendid band
of followers went towards him: they thanked
God, rejoiced in their lord, that they could see
him safe and sound.

*(1629–1643) He is relieved of his armour by the
side of the now calm lake, and his followers go back
with him to Hrothgar's hall, radiant with victory.
Four of them have hard work to carry the monster's
head on a pole.*

Then the helmet and the corslet were quickly
1630 loosened from the valiant one; the lake grew
calm, the water beneath the clouds, stained
with the blood of battle. Thence they went forth
along the foot-worn tracks: glad in their hearts,
the men of kingly courage measured the country
ways, the well-known roads. With difficulty for
1635 each one of those high heroes they bore the head
from off the sea-girt cliff; four of them had much
trouble to bear into the princely hall the head
of Grendel on the spear. So at last there came,
1640 presently advancing to the hall, fourteen Geats,
bold and warlike, and the lord of men among

them, proud in the multitude, trod the meadows
to the mead-hall.

*(1644–1650) Arrived at the hall, Beowulf enters
in triumph to greet Hrothgar. Grendel's head is also
brought into the hall, a thing of horror to the queen
and the assembled nobles.*

Then entered in the chief of the thanes, the
1645 man valiant in deeds, exalted with renown, the
hero bold in battle, to greet Hrothgar. Then was
Grendel's head borne by the hair on to the
chamber-floor, where people drank, a fearful
thing before the nobles and the queen with them,
1650 a wondrous spectacle. Men gazed upon it.

XXIV AND XXV

BEOWULF TELLS OF HIS ADVENTURES, AND HROTHGAR FOLLOWS WITH A DIDACTIC SPEECH. AFTER BANQUETING AND A NIGHT'S REST, THE GEATS GET READY TO GO

[Lines 1651–1739; 1740–1816]

*(1651–1670) Beowulf lays before the king his
trophies, the monster's head and the sword-hilt, and
relates how narrowly he escaped defeat and death,
—how Hrunting failed him in his hour of need, and
he was guided by the good providence of God to see
another sword hanging on the wall of the chamber,
wherewith he killed the mother of Grendel and cut*

off the head of the dead Grendel as well. As the
sword-blade was completely eaten away by the blood
of the two water-sprites, Beowulf could only bring
away the hilt as a trophy.

Beowulf, son of Ecgtheow, spoke. "Behold,
"we have brought thee with gladness, O son of
"Healfdene, ruler of the Scyldings, these sea-
"spoils which thou lookest on here, in token of
1655 "success. I narrowly escaped with my life in fight
"under the water; I dared the work with diffi-
"culty; almost had my struggling ceased, if God
"had not protected me. I could do nothing in the
1660 "fray with Hrunting, trusty though that weapon
"be. Howbeit the Ruler of men granted me that
"I might see hanging in beauty on the wall a
"huge old sword (often and often has He
"guided those who are deprived of friends), so
"that I drew that weapon. Then,—as occasion
1665 "favoured me,—I smote in fight the guardians
"of the dwelling. Then the war-blade, the chased
"sword, was burnt up as the blood burst forth,
"hottest of battle-gore. The hilt I bore away
"thence from the foes; I avenged the outrages—
1670 "the slaughter of the Danes—as it was meet."

(1671–1676) Now is the slaughter of the Danes
avenged; now may Hrothgar sleep fearlessly in
Heorot, quiet and secure as at the first.

"I promise thee, then, that thou mayest sleep

"in Heorot free from care amid thy band of
"nobles and each of the retainers among thy
"people, the older warriors and the younger:
1675 "—so that thou, lord of the Scyldings, needest not
"fear for them, the nobles, murderous attacks
"from that quarter, as thou didst aforetime."

*(1677–1698) The golden hilt is then handed to
and examined by Hrothgar; it has graven on it the
destruction of the race of giants by the flood, and
an inscription in runic letters showing for whom it
had been made.*

Then was the golden hilt, the ancient work of
giants, given into the hand of the old warrior, the
hoary battle-chief; it came into the Danish lord's
.680 possession after the downfall of the demons, a
work of cunning craftsmen:—for when the
hostile-hearted being, God's adversary, guilty of
great crime,—his mother too—quitted this
1685 world, it passed into the power of the best earthly
king between the seas of those who dealt out
money gifts in the Northland. Hrothgar discoursed; he scrutinized the hilt, the ancient
heirloom, upon which was inscribed the rise of
1690 the primeval strife when the flood, the rushing
deep, destroyed the brood of giants. They
suffered terribly; that was a race alien from the
eternal Lord, (and) for that the Sovereign Ruler
gave them a final retribution by the surging
1695 water. Also it was correctly marked in runic

letters, on the sword-guards of pure gold noted
down and said, for whom that sword, choicest
of weapons, with twisted hilt and snake-adorn-
ment, had been made at first.

*(1698–1709) Hrothgar affirms the pre-eminence
of Beowulf, admires his bearing, and confirms his
promises towards him.*

Then the wise son of Healfdene spoke,—
1700 silent was every one! "Lo, this may he affirm who
"furthers truth and right among the people, the
"aged guardian of the land who remembers all,
"far back—that this noble was most well born.
"Beowulf, my friend, thy fame is raised on high
1705 "over each nation far and wide. Thou dost carry
"all this might of thine with calmness and dis-
"creetness of spirit. I will fulfil my compact
"with thee, according as we two arranged before
"in talk. Thou shalt become the perpetual stay
"of thy people—a help of fighters."

*(1709–1722) He refers to the behaviour of the
Danish king Heremod, a cruel and ungenerous tyrant,
as a contrast to that of Beowulf.*

"Not thus was Heremod to Ecgwela's progeny,
1710 "the glorious Scyldings. He did not flourish for
"the joy, but for the slaughter and the violent
"death of Danish folk. He killed his boon com-
"panions in his rage, his bosom friends, till he,

1715 "notorious prince, turned him from human joys
"alone.   Although the mighty God exalted him
"above all men with the joys of power and
"strength, and helped him on, still there grew
"up within his heart a savage spirit; never gave
1720 "he presents to the Danes, that he might obtain
"glory.   Joyless he lived, so that he suffered
"misery for his violence, the lasting pain."

*(1722-1739)   Heremod's history points a moral.
God sometimes gives a man great prosperity,—everything seems in his favour.*

"Do thou instruct thyself by that: know thou
"what manly virtue is. I, wise from my many
"winters, have told this tale on thy account. It is
1725 "a wondrous thing to say how mighty God deals
"out to mankind wisdom, lands and rank, by His
"vast spirit. He has control of all. Sometimes He
"allows the spirit of a man of famous stock to
1730 "wander in delight: gives him in his native land
"enjoyment of this world, a fencèd fortress of
"men to hold; makes regions of the world, a
"spacious empire, subject to him in such wise
"that in his folly he himself thinks it will never
"end. He lives in plenty; nothing—sickness nor
1735 "old age—stands in his way. No trouble caused
"by malice clouds his thoughts, nor does strife
"bring about deadly warfare anywhere, but all
"the world moves to his will."

(1739-1757)   Until a time comes when his sense

of what is due to others becomes torpid, to his great
peril, and arrogance takes possession of him. He
cannot resist the promptings of the evil one. All he
has seems too little. He covets, and neglects the great
duty of giving, forgetful of God's bounty to him and
of his future state. One day he drops out of his place,
and is succeeded by another who wins a well-earned
security by lavish gifts.

1740 "He knows no worse estate [XXV] until a
"measure of overbearing pride waxes and grows
"in him, when the warder, the soul's guardian,
"sleeps. That sleep is too sound, hedged in with
"cares: the slayer is very close, who from the
"wingèd bow shoots with evil intent. Then
1745 "he is struck at the heart, under his armour,
"by the piercing arrow,—the crooked mysterious
"promptings of the accursed sprite. He cannot
"defend himself. What he had held for a long
"time seems to him too little. He covets, hostile
"in mind; never gives, in proud rejoicing, circlets
1750 "overlaid with gold. No thought has he about the
"world to come, and he disdains the share of
"honours God, the Lord of Glory, gave him in
"time past. It happens after, as the final act, that
"the transitory body droops and falls as fore-
1755 "ordained; another, who gives out ornaments
"and ancient possessions of the princes reck-
"lessly, succeeds him; *he* is not troubled with
"fear."

(*1758–1768*) *So Hrothgar exhorts Beowulf not to*

be arrogant or unmindful (like Heremod) of the
future. His flourishing-time will last for a while, and
then death will come.

"Against such evil rancour guard thyself,
"dear Beowulf, best of men; choose that better
"part, thy lasting profit.

1760 "Incline not to arrogance, famous warrior!
"Now shall the fullness of thy strength last for a
"while. But soon after it shall be, that malady or
"sword shall cut thee off from power, or the em-
"brace of fire or welling of a flood, or onset with
1765 "the knife, or arrow's flight, or hideous old age.
"Or brightness of eyes shall diminish and grow
"dim, and at length it shall be that death shall
"overpower thee, noble chieftain!"

(1769–1784) He himself had been king for fifty
years, prosperous and happy; and then Grendel
suddenly appeared—a constant trouble. But now,
thank God, he is permitted to look on the monster's
severed head. He bids Beowulf take part in the
banqueting and promises him much treasure on the
morrow.

"Thus have I ruled the Ring-Danes fifty years
1770 "under the heavens, and have protected them in
"war from many a tribe with spear and sword
"the whole world over; so that I did not believe
"that I had any foe under the breadth of heaven.
"And lo! A change from this came to me in my
1775 "land, sorrow succeeding joy, since Grendel,

"ancient foe, became my visitant. By reason of
"this harrying I suffered constantly much grief
"of mind. And so, thanks be to the Creator,
"the eternal God, for what I have gained while
1780 "still alive,—that with mine eyes I gaze upon
"this blood-stained head, the age-long struggling
"past!

"Go now to thy seat, take part in the joy of
"banqueting, honoured for thy valour. Exceed-
"ing many treasures will I share with thee when
"to-morrow comes."

(*1785–1802*)   *After the banquet Hrothgar and
the tired-out Beowulf retire to rest.*

1785   The Geat was glad at heart, and went straightway to seek his seat, as the sage king enjoined
him. Then, as before, goodly provision was arranged afresh for the heroic warriors sitting in
hall. The shroud of night grew thicker—dark
1790 over the noble company. The whole band rose,
the grey-haired patriarch-Scylding would fain go
to his bed. Exceeding much did the Geat, the
brave shield-warrior, desire to rest. Straightway
1795 the chamberlain, who in courtesy looked after all
a noble's needs—such needs as at that day warrior
travellers used to have—guided him forth, weary
with his adventure, come from far. Then the
noble-hearted man reposed ; the chamber towered
1800 aloft, spacious and gold-adorned. The stranger
slept within, until the swarthy raven, blithe of
heart, harbingered the radiance of heaven.

*(1802–1816) With the return of day a great
yearning comes to Beowulf and his party to go back
to their fatherland. They prepare for the voyage, and
Beowulf gives back the sword Hrunting to Unferth
with courteous thanks, and goes to the hall to say a
few last words to the king.*

Then bright light of morning came hurrying
after the shadows. The warriors hastened. The
1805 nobles were eager to go back to their people, the
mighty-hearted visitor wished to return to his
ship, far from thence. Then the brave man
ordered Hrunting to be brought to the son of
Ecglaf—bade him take his sword, his precious
1810 weapon; he (Beowulf) expressed his thanks to
him for that loan,—said that he counted it a
trusty friend in battle, doughty in war; no whit
did he blame the sword's edge with his words.
A noble warrior was he! And when the warriors
1815 eager to depart were ready in their mail, the
noble honoured by the Danes went to the high
seat where the other was. The hero bold in
fight greeted Hrothgar.

XXVI

BEOWULF'S PARTING SPEECH AND HROTHGAR'S
REPLY. THE LEAVE-TAKING

[Lines 1817–1887]

*(1817–1839) Beowulf informs the king of his
pending departure, thanks him for all his kindness,*

and promises him substantial help in case of any
new emergency, and if he wishes it, an introduction
for his son Hrethric at the Geatish court.

Beowulf, son of Ecgtheow, spoke: "Now we
"seafarers, come from far, desire to say that we
1820 "intend to go to Hygelac. We have been treated
"here quite after our desires,—thou hast served
"us well. If then I can by any means gain on
"earth more of thy heart's affection, lord of men,
1825 "than I have so far done, ready I'll be at once for
"warlike deeds. If I learn this across the circuit
"of the sea,—that those around thy borders
"threaten harm, as enemies have done in times
1830 "gone by, I'll bring a thousand thanes and heroes
"to thy help. As for Hygelac, lord of the Geats, I
"know, though he is young, that he, his people's
"shepherd, will further me by word and deed, so
"that I may show my esteem for thee by deeds,
1835 "and bring to thy rescue my shafted spear, the
"succour of my might, when thou hast need of
"men.
    "And then if Hrethric, the king's son, decides
"to come to Geatish courts, he shall find friends
"in plenty there;—for him who has good parts
"himself, far lands are visited with greater good."

(1840–1865) Hrothgar replies, praising Beowulf's
discretion and indicating him as a possible and
promising successor to Hygelac. He has brought it
to pass that there is peace between the Geats and

Danes, where formerly there was enmity. This peace Hrothgar will do his best to strengthen.

1840   Hrothgar addressed him in return: "The wise "Lord put these speeches in thy mind. Never "heard I a man talk more discreetly at so young "an age; strong art thou in thy might and ripe
1845 "in mind, wise in thy spoken words. I count "it probable, if it falls out that spear or battle "fierce and grim, disease or knife, takes off "the son of Hrethel, takes thy prince, the "shepherd of thy people, and thou hast thy life,
1850 "that the sea-roving Geats would have no better "man to choose as king, as treasure-guard of "warriors, than thyself, if thou dost will to rule "the kingdom of thy kin. Thy spirit pleases me "more as time goes on, dear Beowulf.

1855   "Thou hast effected that to both the nations— "Spear-Danes and people of the Geats,—there "shall be peace in common; wars shall cease, the "vengeful enmities which erewhile they endured; "that while I govern this wide realm, there shall
1860 "be interchange of treasure. And many a man "shall greet his fellow with good things across "the water's expanse where the gannet flies; the "ringed ship shall bring over the seas gifts and "tokens of regard. I know the people are of
1865 "steadfast build, both in their dealings with "friend and foe, blameless in all respects, after "old custom."

(*1866–1880*) *The aged king gives Beowulf twelve*

*costly gifts and weeps at his leave-taking, overcome
with emotion at the thought that he may never see
him again.*

Then did the protector of nobles, Healfdene's
son, give him within the hall twelve valued
gifts, and bade him go in health, visit his own
1870 dear people, quickly return again. Then the
king, noble in lineage, the Scyldings' prince,
kissed the best of thanes, and clasped him round
the neck,—tears streamed down the face of the
grey-haired warrior. Very old and wise, he had
thoughts of two issues, but knew one was more
1875 likely—that they would never be allowed to
see each other more, brave men in council. The
man was so beloved by him that he could not
hold back his surging sorrow: but in his bosom,
fast in the bonds of his heart, a secret longing
1880 after the dear man burned in his blood.

*(1880–1887) So Beowulf, rejoicing in the rich
bounty of the king, sets off, accompanied by his men.
All praise the munificence of Hrothgar.*

Then Beowulf, champion brave with gold,
exulting in his treasure, trod the greensward;
the ship, which rode at anchor, waited its owning
lord. Then, as they went, was Hrothgar's bounti-
1885 fulness often praised. That was an altogether
blameless king, until old age deprived him of the
joys of power,—old age which has oftentimes
caused harm to many.

XXVII

[Lines 1888–1962]

*(1888–1903) Arrived at the water's edge, they
meet the coast-warden, whose courteous behaviour is
rewarded by a sword from Beowulf. They load the
ship with their armour and presents.*

Thus to the water came the troop of most
courageous liegemen :—ring-mail they wore,
1890 corslets interlocked. The land-guard perceived
the nobles coming back, as he had done before ;
not with contumely did he hail the visitors from
off the headland's brow, but rode up towards
them and said that they, the bright-mailed
1895 warriors who went to their ships, would be
welcomed on their return by the people of the
Geats.

Then was the spacious sea-boat on the beach
laden with battle-gear, the ship with curved
prow was loaded with horses and valuables ;
the mast towered above Hrothgar's hoarded
treasures.

1900   To the boat-keeper Beowulf gave a sword
bound round with gold, so that henceforth he
was more honoured on the mead-bench for that
treasure,—that heirloom.

(1903–1913) So they depart, and after a prosperous voyage arrive at the land of the Geats.

Then the ship went on, to ruffle the deep
1905 water; it left the Danish land. Then to the mast
a sail, a mighty sea-cloth, was fastened by a
sheet; the wave-borne timbers groaned, the wind
over the billows did not throw out of her course
the ship floating over the water. The ship jour-
1910 neyed on, with foam at her twisted prow she
floated over the waves, the streams of the sea,
until they could descry the Geatish cliffs, the
well-known headlands. The keel pressed forward,
driven by the wind; it stood upon the land.

*(1914–1919) The haven-watchman hurried to the
beach, from which he had so often gazed seawards
in the hope of sighting Beowulf's ship, and made fast
the craft to the shore.*

The haven-ward was quickly ready at the
1915 water's edge, he who before had long time
looked out eagerly far over the sea for the dear
men. He tethered to the beach the roomy ship,
held fast with anchor-ropes, lest the waves' force
should drive the joyous craft away from them.

*(1920–1931) The treasure is carried up to the
magnificent stronghold, not far from the sea, in
which Hygelac lives with his young and noble wife
Hygd.*

L

1920   Then he bade the jewels and gold plate be
carried up, treasure of nobles; it was not far
thence for him to seek out the giver of riches.
Hygelac, son of Hrethel, sojourns there at home,
himself and his retainers, hard by the sea-wall.
1925   The building was magnificent, the chief a
mighty ruler in the lofty hall; Hygd the queen
very youthful, wise, accomplished, although she,
the daughter of Hæreth, had dwelt but few
winters within the walls of the stronghold. For all
1930 that she was not illiberal, nor too niggardly with
gifts, with costly treasures, to the Geatish people.

EPISODE OF THRYTH

[Lines 1931–1962]

*(1931–1944) The story of Thryth, wife of Offa,
is apparently introduced here in order to heighten
the impression of Hygd's goodness. Modthryth
was proud, suspicious and vengeful. Courtiers who
displeased her were treacherously killed.*

Modthryth, high queen of the people, showed
terrible vindictiveness; no brave man among the
1935   court favourites, except as husband, dared gaze on
her openly with his eyes, but he might count on
deadly bonds being appointed for him, woven by
hand; very soon after his seizure was the knife
brought into service, so that the damasked sword
1940   might settle it,—proclaim the punishment of death.
That is no queenly custom for a woman to practise,
peerless though she may be, that a peace-weaver

should assail the life of a valued liegeman, because of fancied insult. Howbeit the kinsman of Hemming put an end to all this.

(*1945–1962*) *Yet it was said by some that after her marriage with Offa she became less spiteful, and in process of time showed deep love for her husband, the wise and noted Offa, and used her royal estate well.*

1945   Men at their ale-drinking said besides that she brought about less harm to the people, less spiteful vengeance, when once she had been given in marriage, gold-bedecked, to the young champion,
1950   noble in lineage, when she, at her father's bidding, visited in a journey Offa's court over the pale gold sea.

    There, afterwards, she used her fortunes well upon the royal seat, famed for her goodness, while she was alive; she held highest love towards the
1955   prince of heroes, who was of all mankind, as I have heard, of human kin, the best between the seas. Wherefore Offa, spear-bold man, was noted far and wide for gifts and victories, and ruled his native land
1960   with wisdom. Of him was born Eomær, stay of warriors, kinsman of Hemming, grandson of Garmund, mighty in the fray.

XXVIII AND XXIX

BEOWULF'S RECEPTION BY HYGELAC. HE BEGINS TO
TELL THE STORY OF HIS EXPEDITION, BUT
DIVERGES INTO AN EPISODE ABOUT
HROTHGAR'S DAUGHTER FREA-
WARU. AFTERWARDS HE
RESUMES HIS STORY

[Lines 1963–2038; 2039–2143]

(1963–1976) In the morning sunshine Beowulf and his comrades walk from the beach to the stronghold. His coming is quickly announced and preparation is made for his reception, by the King's orders.

Then the hero went forth himself and his companions, by the sand, treading the sea-
1965 beaches, the broad foreshores. The world's lamp shone, the sun hastening from the south;—they passed along their way, went quickly thither, where they heard tell that the protector of nobles, the slayer of Ongentheow, the good young
1970 warrior-king, within the dwellings dealt out rings. Quickly was Beowulf's coming told to Hygelac,—that the warriors' shield, his comrade in arms, had come alive into the precincts and was going on towards the court, safe from the battle.

1975 Forthwith the chamber was prepared within for the warrior-band, as the great ruler ordered.

(1977–1983) After a formal greeting, Beowulf

sits facing Hygelac in hall, and the mead-cup is handed round to the company.

Then he who had escaped in battle sat opposite Hygelac himself, kinsman facing kinsman, after the lord of men had greeted the faithful one 1980 in courtly speech with forceful words. Round the hall Hæreth's daughter went with stoups of mead, cherished the people, and bore the beaker to the warriors' hands.

(1983–1998) The king asks about Beowulf's adventures with much interest, and especially whether his expedition, of which he, the king, had taken a gloomy view, was successful. He thanks God for Beowulf's safe return.

Hygelac began courteously to question his 1985 comrade in the lofty hall—he desired earnestly to know what adventures had befallen the Sea-Geats. "How went it with you on your journey, "much-loved Beowulf, when you suddenly re-"solved to seek a feud far off, across the salt 1990 "water—battle at Heorot? Hast thou any whit "lightened the well-known trouble of Hrothgar, "famous prince? For that I was troubled with "gloomy care, surgings of sorrow; no faith "had I in my loved liege's journey. Long 1995 "time I begged thee, that on no account wouldst "thou go near the murderous monster, but "wouldst let the South-Danes settle their feud

"with Grendel by themselves. I give thanks to
"God that I am suffered to see thee safe and
"sound."

(*1999–2009*) *Beowulf replies that his complete
victory over Grendel has already become known to
many.*

2000   Beowulf, son of Ecgtheow, spake forth: "That
"great encounter is well known to many men,
"lord Hygelac, what a bout of fighting I had
"with Grendel upon that field, where he had
"wrought many and many a sorrow, age-long
2005 "misery, for the victorious Scyldings. I avenged
"it all, so that no kin of Grendel upon earth need
"boast about that uproar in the twilight,—not he
"who, encompassed by crime, lives longest of
"the hateful race."

(*2009–2023*) *First he went to the palace to see
Hrothgar, who gave him a seat of honour. He
describes the banquet which ensued, and how the
queen and Freawaru, the king's daughter, dispensed
hospitality.*

2010   "Once there, I went first to the ring-hall to
"greet Hrothgar. Forthwith the famous son of
"Healfdene, when he knew my purpose, allotted
"me a seat by his own sons. The company was
"joyous; never in my life have I seen under the
2015 "vault of heaven greater joy at mead among men
"sitting in hall. From time to time the illustrious

"queen, the nation's pledge of peace, went up
"and down the hall, pressed the young men to
"feast, and often gave a circlet to some guest, ere
"she went back to her seat. Now and then, before
2020 "the noblest retainers, Hrothgar's daughter bore
"the ale-cup to the warriors from end to end. I
"heard those sitting in hall call her Freawaru, as
"she presented the studded vessel to the heroes."

EPISODE OF FREAWARU

[Lines 2024–2069]

*(2024–2031) The mention of Freawaru leads
the poet into a digression about her betrothal to
Ingeld, son of Froda, king of the Heathobards.
Hrothgar had thought by the match to put an end
to the feuds between the Heathobards and Danes.
Such schemes often fail of their purpose, however.*

2024   "Young and gold-adorned, she was betrothed to
"Froda's gracious son. This had seemed good to the
"friend of the Scyldings, the protector of the king-
"dom,—he counts it good policy—that he should
"settle many deadly feuds and quarrels, through
"that woman. For the most part seldom at all is
"it that the murderous spear lies idle, even for
2030 "a little while, after the downfall of a prince,
"however good the bride may be."

*(2032–2040) In this case, for instance, it was
natural that the Heathobards should have no friendly
feelings towards the noble Danish courtiers who
attended upon Freawaru and who wore armour
captured from their ancestors in war.*

"Then it may well displease the prince of the
"Heathobards and every thane of his nation, when
"he goes with the lady into hall, that the high lords
2035   "of the Danes are gloriously entertained. Upon
"them gleam the heirlooms of their ancestors, hard
"and ring-adorned, which had been the treasure
"of the Heathobards, so long as they might wield
"their weapons [XXIX], until they had led to
2040   "destruction in the fatal play of shields their dear
"companions and their very lives."

(*2041–2056*) *An old Heathobard warrior draws
the attention of Ingeld to the sword with which a
young Dane goes boastfully about in the hall, and
reminds him that it is the one which his father,
Froda, had when he was slain.*

"Then, at the beer-drinking, an aged spearman
"speaks, who eyes an adorned sword, recollects it
"all, the men's death by the spear. His heart is fierce,
"and he begins in gloomy wise to test a young
2045   "campaigner's temper by the musings of his mind,
"to rouse accursed strife, and says these words:
"'Canst thou, my friend, discern the blade, the
"'precious weapon, which thy father bore to
"'battle when he was under helmet for the last
2050   "'time, where the Danes slew him, the brave
"'Scyldings took possession of the field, when
"'Withergyld lay low after the fall of heroes?
"'Now, a son of some one of these slayers goes
"'about here, in our hall, rejoicing in his trap-
2055   "'pings,—boasts of the carnage, wears the adorn-
"'ment you should own by right.'"

*(2057–2069) Thus he goads the young warrior
into avenging his father's death on the Danish
courtier, notwithstanding the treaty between the
Heathobards and Danes, and the old feud breaks
forth anew. So it cannot be expected that peace will
last long between the two tribes.*

"Thus he urges and prompts him time after time
"with bitter words, until the hour comes that on
"account of his father's deeds the woman's retainer
2060 "sleeps bloodstained after the sword-stroke, forfeit
"of his life; the other escapes from thence alive,—
"he knows the country well. Then is the oath of
"the chieftains broken on both sides, when deadly
2065 "hate wells up in Ingeld, and his love for his wife
"grows cooler with the risings of care. Hence I
"count not the faith of the Heathobards, the great
"tribal peace, without deceit towards the Danes,
"nor their friendship stable."

*(2069–2100) To return to Grendel. One night
as Beowulf's party were guarding the hall, Grendel
came and devoured one of them—Hondscio—and
then attacked Beowulf, thinking to carry him off. But
Beowulf was a match for him, and wrenched off his
right hand, whereupon he fled away to die.*

2070 "Now I will proceed and tell again of Grendel,
"that thou, O giver of treasure, mayst fully know
"what was the issue of the hand-to-hand struggle
"of the champions. After the gem of the heavens
"had glided over the earth, the furious spirit, the
"dread ogre of night, came to close with us where

2075 "we, still whole, kept watch over the hall. There
"was battle impending for Hondscio, violent
"death for the doomed man; he, belted cham-
"pion, fell first. For him, my famous brother-
2080 "thane, Grendel was a devouring murderer,—
"he consumed the beloved man's whole body.
"Howbeit the slayer with the blood yet on his
"mouth, intent on evil, would not after that
"leave the gold-hall again empty of hand, but
2085 "first, lusty in strength, he ventured on me—
"would have gripped me with ready hand. His
"glove hung, ample and strange, attached by
"curious clasps,—it was all cunningly contrived
"with great skill and with the skins of dragons.
2090 "Therein he wished, the fierce evil-doer, to put,
"as one of many, me unoffending; thus he could
"not do, as soon as I stood upright in my wrath.
"It is too long to tell how I paid this enemy of
"the people a recompense for all his crimes;
2095 "there, my prince, did I exalt thy nation by my
"works. He slipped away—enjoyed the sweets
"of life a little while: yet his right hand re-
"mained behind at Heorot, and he, sad at heart,
2100 "fell miserably thence to the mere's bottom."

(*2101–2114*) *Next day was given up to feasting
and revelry. The king rewarded Beowulf richly with
presents at the banquet.*

"The Scyldings' kindly lord repaid me richly
"for that deadly fight, with beaten gold,—with

"many treasures—when the morrow came and
"we had sat down to the banquet. There was
2105 "singing and merriment. The patriarch Scylding,
"who had heard of so many things, told of by-
" gone times; now and again a man brave in
"battle touched his joyful harp of wood with
"happy effect. Sometimes he told a true and
2110 "mournful tale; anon the generous king re-
"hearsed aright a strange adventure; then again
"after that the veteran battle-chief, trammelled
"by his age, would make lament over his past
"youthful days and strength in battle. His heart
"was moved within him, as he, old in years,
"brought much of the past to mind."

*(2115–2130) On the ensuing night came Grendel's
mother, bent on avenging her son, already dead. She
killed a trusty Danish counsellor, Æschere, and dragged
him off to her watery home.*

2115 "Thus we took our pleasure therein the live-
"long day, until another night ensued for men.
"Then, after that, was Grendel's mother quickly
"ready for revenge; she journeyed full of care.
"Death,—war-hate of the Geats—had cut off
2120 "her son. The monstrous hag avenged her child,
"boldly she laid a warrior low; there was the life
"parted from Æschere, the sage old counsellor.
"Nor could the people of the Danes, when morn-
2125 "ing had come, burn his body after death, nor lay
"the beloved man on the funeral pyre. She bore

"away the body in her fiendish grasp, under
"the mountain stream. That was the bitterest
"of griefs for Hrothgar, out of all those which
2130 "long had befallen the people's prince."

*(2131–2143)   On an appeal from the anguish-
stricken Hrothgar, who promised him reward, Beowulf sought out the monster in the depths of the lake
and killed her, narrowly escaping with his life. He
received much treasure from Hrothgar.*

"Then, sad at heart, the sovereign begged me
"by thy life, that I would show prowess in the
"swirls of waters, risk my life, do heroic deeds;
"he promised me reward.
2135   " Then, as is widely known, I found the grim
"and terrible guardian of the welling water's
"depths. There we were awhile, hand to hand;
"the water boiled with blood; and I with mighty
"blade cut off the head of Grendel's mother in
2140 "the subterranean hall. Thence with my life I
"hardly got away. I was not doomed as yet; but
"Healfdene's son, the protector of nobles, gave
"me thereafter many treasures."

XXXI

END OF BEOWULF'S STORY. HE HANDS OVER HIS
PRESENTS TO THE KING AND QUEEN AND RE-
CEIVES OTHERS FROM HYGELAC. AFTER
THE DEATH OF HYGELAC AND HIS SON
HEARDRED, BEOWULF BECOMES KING
AND REIGNS PEACEABLY UNTIL A
CERTAIN DRAGON APPEARS,
THE GUARDIAN OF A HOARD
OF TREASURE

[Lines 2144–2220]

*(2144–2176) Hrothgar was indeed true to the
old traditions with his lavish gifts, all of which
Beowulf hands over to Hygelac, to whom he owes
everything, and to his queen Hygd.*

"So lived the people's king, according to good
2145 "customs. By no means did I lack the rewards,
"the meed of might: but he, the son of Healf-
"dene, gave me treasures at my own choice,
"which I will bring to thee, heroic king, and
2150 "offer gladly. All of my joys still depend on
"thee; I have few near-relatives save thee,
"O Hygelac!"

Then he bade them bear in a boar's head
banner, a helmet towering in battle, a grey
corslet, a splendid war-sword, and then pronounced this speech:—

2155   "Hrothgar, the wise prince, gave this battle-
"gear to me: in language clear bade me that first

"of all I should acquaint thee with its history.
"He said that King Hiorogar, Scylding lord, had
"it long time; yet he would not for all that give
2160 "it—the breast-armour—to his son, the valiant
"Heoroward, true as he might be to him. En-
"joy it all well!"

I heard that four bay horses, swift and exactly
2165 alike, followed in the track of the armour,—he
gave him possession of the steeds and treasures.
So should a kinsman do, and never weave
a cunning snare for another, or contrive death
2170 for his bosom friend by secret craft. His
nephew was most true to Hygelac, the brave
in battle, and each was mindful of the other's
good.

I heard that he presented to Hygd the circlet,
that curious, wondrous jewel, which Wealhtheow, the prince's daughter, had given him, and
2175 three horses as well, graceful and bright with
saddlery; thenceforward was her breast adorned,
after receiving the ring.

*(2177–2189)   Beowulf's character is described and
praised.   For a long time he was underrated by his
countrymen.*

Thus the son of Ecgtheow, the man renowned
in war, showed himself doughty in brave deeds.
He bore himself honourably, never struck down
2180 his boon companions at the drinking; his was no
brutal mind, but he, the brave in battle, guarded

with the greatest human art the liberal gifts
which God had granted him. For a long time he
was contemned, as the children of the Geats
knew him not to be brave, nor would the lord of
2185 the Geats do him much honour at the mead-
bench. They very much suspected he was sloth-
ful, a feeble princeling; but to the glorious man
there came a reversal of all afflictions.

(2190–2199) Hygelac's princely gifts to Beowulf.

2190   Then the protector of warriors, the king of
martial glory, bade Hrethel's legacy be brought
in, decked with gold; there was not at that time
among the Geats a greater treasure in the shape
of a sword. That he laid in Beowulf's lap, and
2195 gave him seven thousand (hides of land), a hall,
and the rank of chief. To both of them alike had
land descended in that country—an estate and
inherited right: but a great kingdom belonged
rather to the one who was higher in rank.

PART II

BEOWULF AND THE DRAGON

[Lines 2200–3182]

(*2200–2220*) *After the death of Hygelac and his son Heardred, Beowulf becomes king and reigns fifty years. Then a dragon, the guardian of a hoard of treasure, rises up to torment the nation.*

2200 AFTERWARDS, in later days, it fell out through the tumult of battles thus. When Hygelac lay low and battle-blades were the death of Heardred, in spite of the sheltering shield,

2205 when the martial Scyldings, hardy war-wolves, sought him out among his conquering people, and attacked the nephew of Hereric in force,— then after that, the spacious realm came into the hands of Beowulf. He ruled it well for fifty win-

2210 ters—that was an aged king, a veteran guardian of his people,—until in the dark nights a certain one began to have power,—a dragon, who on an upland heath kept watch over a hoard, a high stone-barrow. Below there lay a path unknown to men.

2215   Into that place went some man or other [Here follow six imperfect lines now partly illegible, apparently to the effect that the man took some

2220 of the monster's hoard while he was asleep, and roused his anger.]

XXXII

THE HISTORY OF THE HOARD AND HOW THE
DRAGON WAS ROBBED. THE DRAGON'S
VENGEANCE

[Lines 2221–2311]

(2221–2270) The man who first came upon the hoard was an outlaw who thought to take refuge in the cave. He stood aghast at the wealth of treasure round him—the rich spoils of a past generation of warriors, placed there by the last survivor of a noble company, who bewails his loneliness in a famous elegy.

By no means had he purposely, of his own accord, sought out the dragon's hoard,—he who injured him sorely,—but under stress of need the slave of some one or other of the sons of
2225 men fled from vengeful blows, lacking a home, and entered therein, a sin-perplexed soul. Soon it happened that grisly horror rose up
2230 in the stranger [four more lines imperfect]. While terror held him, he saw the treasure-chest. There in that earthly house were many of such ancient heirlooms as some man or other in days
2235 of yore had cautiously hid there, the vast legacy of a noble race, precious treasures. Death had carried them off in times now past, and then that one of the people's chieftains who lived longest, a guardian gloomy at the loss of friends,
2240 expected the same fate—that he might own for but a little space the slowly gathered treasures.

M

A barrow stood all ready to hand on open
ground, near where the billows surged, hard
by a cape, new-made, secured by binding spells.
2245 Into that place the keeper of the jewels had
borne a vast amount of the princely wealth, the
plated gold worthy of being hoarded. He said
these few words:—"Now do thou, O Earth,
"hold fast what heroes might not,—the posses-
"sions of nobles. Lo! Brave men won it at first
2250 "from thee; death in war, horrid carnage, took
"away every one of my tribe who yielded up this
"life; they saw (the last of) festive joy. I have no
"one to bear sword, or to burnish the plated
"flagon, the precious drinking-cup; the noble
"warriors have departed to another place. Now
2255 "will the hard helmet, bedight with gold, be de-
"prived of its adornments; they sleep who should
"burnish the battle-masks. The armour too,
"which stood the stroke of swords in battle,
"mid the crash of shields, perishes as does the
2260 "fighter; nor may the ringed mail fare far and
"wide with the warrior, side by side with mighty
"men. There is no joy of harp, no pastime with
"the gladdening lute; no good hawk sweeps
"through the hall, nor does the swift steed paw
2265 "the courtyard. Baleful death has banished hence
"many of the human race."

Thus with sad heart he mourned his troubles,
alone after them all, and sorrowfully paced about
by day and night, until death's rising tide
2270 touched at his heart.

*(2270–2277) The hoard was unprotected when
the dragon discovered it. Although it could do him
no good, he mounted guard over it.*

The ancient twilight-foe found the delightful
treasure standing open; he who seeks out barrows, flies by night, the smooth malicious dragon,
burning and wrapped in flame: sorely the
2275 people of the country dread him. He was fated
to seek out the hoard under the earth, where, old
in winters, he must keep watch over the heathen
gold,—and not be one whit the better for it.

*(2278–2286) The outlaw seizes a precious goblet
and buys the favour of his lord therewith. The hoard
is ransacked.*

Thus this scourge of the people had for three
hundred winters occupied in the earth a mighty
2280 treasure-house, until a certain man enraged him
in his heart; bore to his over-lord the plated
goblet, and begged his master for conditions of
peace. Then was the hoard ransacked, the hoard
of jewels carried off, his boon was granted to
2285 the wretched man. For the first time the lord
examined the ancient work of men.

*(2287–2302) The dragon awakes, and becomes
aware that an enemy has been in his cave, and
despoiled him of treasure.*

As soon as the dragon woke, there sprang up
strife; he hastened along the rock, the strong-

hearted beast discovered the footprints of the foe
—he had walked forwards and close to the head
2290 of the dragon with his stealthy craft. Thus may
an undoomed man,—one who retains the favour
of the Almighty, lightly pass through both woe
and banishment. The guardian of the hoard
searched with care over the ground, he wished
to find the man who had done him this injury
2295 in his sleep: glowing and fierce at heart he
went completely round the barrow oftentimes;
there was not any man there, in that deserted
place. Still he had joyful thoughts of fighting
—of the work of battle. At times he turned back
into the barrow, looked for the costly vessel.
2300 Soon he discovered this,—that one of mortal
kind had searched out the gold, the splendid
treasures.

*(2302–2311)   He waits for the night in order
to take vengeance, and then ravages the country with
fire.*

The guardian of the hoard waited with difficulty till evening came. Then was the lord of
the barrow bursting with rage, the evil beast
2305 meant to requite with fire the theft of the costly
drinking-bowl. Then day departed, as the dragon
wished; no longer would he watch upon the side
of the barrow, but he went forth with flame,
furnished with fire! The beginning was fearful
2310 for the country folk, and it had an end, speedily

and sorely, in the person of their bounteous Lord.

XXXIII

DEVASTATION BY THE DRAGON. BEOWULF, WHOSE
PAST HISTORY IS SHORTLY RECITED,
DETERMINES TO FIGHT HIM
SINGLE-HANDED

[Lines 2312–2390]

(2312–2333) The whole country-side is consumed by the fire from the dragon's mouth; even Beowulf's stronghold is attacked by the flames. He fears that he must have displeased Almighty God, and sinks into unwonted dejection.

Then the fiend began to vomit forth flames, to burn the noble dwellings; the gleam of fire blazed forth, a terror to the sons of men; the
2315 hateful creature flying in the air would leave there no thing with life. The serpent's warfare was widely visible, the vengeance of the devastator far and near—how the warlike enemy hated and humbled the Geat people. He hastened
2320 back to his hoard again, his secret hall, ere the time of day; he had surrounded the people of the land with fire, with flame and burning. He trusted in his barrow, his fighting powers and wall,—and his trust played him false! Then was the horror made known to Beowulf, quickly and
2325 truly, that his own home, best of buildings, the

princely seat of the Geats, was being swallowed
by the waves of fire. That was a grief for the
brave man's soul, greatest of heart-sorrows. The
wise chief supposed that he had sorely angered
2330 the Almighty, the everlasting Lord, contrary to
the eternal law; within him his breast was
troubled with gloomy thoughts, which was not
customary for him.

(2333–2354) *He has a fireproof shield of iron made
for himself, and disdaining the help of an army,
determines to fight the dragon single-handed, no less
daring in his old age than when he quelled Grendel
and his dam.*

The flaming dragon had wasted with fire the
stronghold of the people, the land by the sea,
2335 all that region of earth. For that the warlike king,
the Geats' prince, contrived vengeance against
him. The warriors' protector, chief of nobles,
then bade a curious shield, all iron, be made
for him; he knew full well that forest-wood—
2340 a linden shield—could not avail him against
flame. The most excellent prince was doomed to
meet with the end of his transitory days—of this
world's life—and the serpent as well, though
he had held the hoarded treasure long.
2345   Then did the lord of rings disdain to seek out
with a host, an ample army, the creature who
flew far and wide. He did not fear the battle for
himself, nor did he count for anything the ser-

pent's fighting-powers, his strength and courage.
2350 For he, bold in extremity erewhile, had passed
through many contests,—victorious through the
tumult of battles—after he had purged Hrothgar's hall, and crushed in combat Grendel's kin,
of hated race.

(2354-2366) *Then again that was no mean
encounter in which Hygelac was slain, and from
which Beowulf escaped by swimming, defending himself as he went.*

2354 Not least was that of hand-to-hand encounters, in which Hygelac was slain, when the Geat
king, the gracious lord of peoples, son of
Hrethel, died a bloody death in Friesland, struck
down by the sword, in the rush of battle. Thence
2360 Beowulf had got away by his own strength,
used his power of swimming—alone he had on
his arm thirty battle-dresses, when he plunged
in the sea. The Hetware, who, bearing their
shields, went forth against him, had no cause to
2365 boast about their fight on foot; few got them
back again from that war-wolf to see their homes.

(2367-2379) *On his return to his country, the
widowed queen had offered him the throne, which he
refused. So the young Heardred, the son of Hygelac,
became king and Beowulf had generously helped him
with his counsel.*

Thus did the son of Ecgtheow swim back to

his people over the sea's expanse, a wretched
solitary wanderer. There Hygd offered him
2370 wealth and a kingdom, treasure and a royal
throne; she trusted not her child, that he could
hold the royal seats against foreign armies,
now that Hygelac was dead. But none the more
could the bereaved people bring the noble
2375 chief on any conditions to be Heardred's lord,
or to be willing to accept the kingly dignity.
Still he upheld him among the people by friendly
counsel, kindly and with respect, until he grew
older,—ruled the Geats.

(*2379–2390*) *Eanmund and Eadgils, banished
nephews of the Swedish King Onela, come to
Heardred's court for shelter. For this Onela killed
Heardred, but allowed Beowulf to succeed to the
throne.*

2379   Banished men, sons of Ohthere, sought him
out from over sea,—they had rebelled against
the protector of the Scylfings, the best of the
sea-kings who in Sweden gave out treasure—
a famous prince. That was his life's limit: he,
2385 son of Hygelac, in return for his hospitality,
had as his lot a deadly wound by thrustings
of the sword, and Ongentheow's son went
back again to seek his home when Heardred
lay low, and suffered Beowulf to occupy the
2390 throne and rule the Geats. He was a noble
king!

XXXIV

BEOWULF'S VENGEANCE ON ONELA. HE SETS
OUT TO FIGHT THE DRAGON, AND TALKS
OF HIS PAST LIFE IN A FAREWELL
SPEECH

[Lines 2391–2459]

(*2391–2396*) *Beowulf avenged Heardred's death
by helping Eadgils, who kills Onela.*

He took care to requite the people's loss in
later days; he became the friend of the deserted
Eadgils, he supported the son of Ohthere over
2395 the wide sea with an army, with warriors and
weapons, avenged him afterwards with cam-
paigns fraught with disaster and distress; he
deprived the king of life.

(*2397–2416*) *Now he goes with twelve attendants
to reconnoitre, having learned about the dragon's cave
from the outlaw who first discovered it.*

So the son of Ecgtheow got safely through
each one of the attacks, the savage feuds, the
desperate encounters, until that day on which he
2400 had to do battle with the serpent. Then the
lord of the Geats went, with twelve others,
bursting with rage, to look upon the dragon. He
had learnt then from whence the feud arose, the
hate baleful to men,—the famous treasure vessel
2405 had come into his possession by the hand of the

finder. This man who had brought about the beginning of the quarrel was the thirteenth man of the company, a wretched captive; thither he had humbly to lead the way. Against his will he 2410 went to the point where he knew of a certain earthy chamber, a vault under the ground, hard by the surgings of the sea, the strife of waters, which was full within of gems and filigrees. The hideous guardian, a fighter ready for battle, long 2415 time under the earth had guarded the golden treasures;—property not easy for any man to get possession of.

(2417–2424) Seated upon a headland, full of gloomy forebodings, Beowulf makes a farewell speech to his companions.

So the king bold in war sat on the headland, and from that place the Geats' generous lord spake words of greeting to his retainers. His 2420 spirit was sad, restless and ready to depart. The fate was immeasurably near which was to wait upon the aged man, to seek the treasure of his soul, to part asunder life from body; not long after that was the spirit of the prince enwrapped in flesh.

(2425–2443) First he tells how in his early youth he was a favourite at King Hrethel's court, and how one of the king's sons treacherously slew the other, whose death remained unavenged.

2425 Beowulf, son of Ecgtheow, spoke: "In my
"youth I passed through many battle-charges,
"times of war; I remember it all. I was seven
"winters old when the lord of treasures, the
"gracious ruler of peoples, received me from my
2430 "father. King Hrethel had and kept me, gave me
"wealth and food, bore in mind our kinship.
"Never through life was I a whit less liked by
"him as a warrior within the stronghold than
"were any of his sons—Herebeald and Hæthcyn
2435 "or my own Hygelac. For the eldest a bed of
"death was undeservedly prepared by the action
"of his kinsman: for Hæthcyn struck him down,
"—his lord and friend—by an arrow from his
"horn-tipped bow; he missed the mark and shot
2440 "his kinsman—one brother the other—with his
"bloody shaft. That was an onset beyond com-
"pensation, exceedingly sinful, wearying to the
"heart; and yet for all that, the prince had to
"quit life unavenged."

(2444–2459) *The piteous case of a father who loses
a son by a violent death is portrayed in one elegiac
passage.*

"So it is painful to an old man to suffer that
2445 "his son should swing upon the gallows in his
"youth; he may utter then a dirge, a doleful
"song, when his son hangs as a sport for the
"raven, and he, old, stricken in years, can frame
2450 "no help for him. Unceasingly, at every morn,

"he is reminded of the passing of his son; he
"cares not to wait for another son and heir
"within his stronghold, when one has had his
"fill of deeds in the shape of a violent death.
2455 "With sorrow and care he sees in his son's dwell-
"ing the festive hall abandoned, the windswept
"resting-place bereft of joy: the riders sleep,
"the champions, in the grave; there is no sound
"of harp, no merry-making in the courts, as
"once there was."

XXXV

BEOWULF ENDS HIS DISCOURSE AND GOES FORTH TO
ATTACK THE DRAGON. THE FIGHT BEGINS

[Lines 2460–2601]

*(2460–2479) Hrethel renounces the joys of life and
passes the rest of his days in solitary sadness. At his
death he leaves everything to his sons.*

2460   "So he goes to his chamber and sings alone a
"sorrowful lay for the other; everything seems
"too spacious for him, both fields and dwelling-
"place. In like manner the protector of the
"Geats bore surging sorrow in his heart for
2465 "Herebeald; he could not in any wise avenge
"that feud upon the slayer; none the sooner
"could he pursue the warrior with hostile acts,
"though he was not beloved by him. Thus he
"gave up the joys of men, with sorrow in his
"heart, when that grief befell him: he chose

2470   "God's light. He left to his sons, when he with-
"drew from life, the land and stronghold, as a
"wealthy man does.

  "Then was there conflict and strife between
"the Swedes and Geats, a common feud across
"the broad water, harsh enmity, after Hrethel
2475   "was dead. And the sons of Ongentheow were
"vigorous and warlike,—no wish had they to
"seek the peace across the lakes, but near
"Hreosnabeorh planned oftentimes a dire and
"treacherous trap."

(2479–2489) *Then the Swedes attacked the
country, and killed Hæthcyn. In revenge, Eofor killed
the Swedish king Ongentheow.*

  "That—the feud and outrage—did my
2480   "friendly kinsmen avenge, as was well known,
"though one of them paid for it with his life,—a
"hard bargain. To Hæthcyn, lord of the Geats,
"the fight was fatal. Then, at morn, as I have
"been told, one brother avenged the other on
2485   "the slayer with the edge of the sword, where
"Ongentheow met with Eofor; the helm of
"battle split asunder, faint from a sword-stroke
"fell the aged Scylfing. His hand remembered
"feuds enough, it kept not back the fatal blow."

(2490–2509) *Hygelac gave Beowulf lands and
other possessions, and Beowulf repaid him by keeping
his sword always at the king's disposal, so that he never*

needed to hire mercenary officers from abroad. One of Beowulf's exploits was the slaughter of Dæghrefn, a warrior of the Hugas, whom he killed by clasping him in his powerful arms.

2490   "I paid back the treasures which he (Hygelac)
"had given me, in battle, by my gleaming sword,
"as was permitted me. He gave me land, a dwel-
"ling place, a glad possession. There was no
"need for him that he should have to seek among
2495 "the Gepidæ or Spear-Danes, or in the Swedish
"realm, a less good warrior,—to purchase him
"with treasure. For him I would always be to the
"fore in the host,—by myself at the front. And so
"through life shall do battle, while this sword
2500 "lasts, which has often done me service, early
"and late, since by valour I became the slayer of
"Dæghrefn, champion of the Hugas. He could
"not bring the adornments, the breast-decora-
2505 "tion, to the Frisian king; but he, the standard-
"bearer, sank in battle, a noble in prowess. Nor
"was the sword his slayer, but my unfriendly
"grasp crushed his body, the surgings of his
"heart.

"Now shall weapon's edge, hand and hard
"sword, do battle for the hoard."

(2510–2537) He announces his intention of going forth at once to the fight. He will not eschew armour as he did when fighting Grendel, but will take a shield and corslet because of the fire proceeding

*from the dragon. He will conquer single-handed
or die. His comrades are to keep watch on the
barrow.*

2510   Beowulf discoursed,—spoke a last time with
words of boasting:—"I ventured on many
"battles in my younger days; once more will I,
"the aged guardian of the people, seek combat
"and get renown, if the evil ravager will meet
2515 me outside his earthy vault." Then he addressed
all of the men, brave under their helmets,
his close companions, for the last time. "I
"would not bear a sword or weapon against the
"serpent, if I knew how else I might come
2520 "to grips with the monster in such manner as
"to fulfil my boast, as I did aforetime against
"Grendel. But there I look for hot destructive
"fire, for blast and venom; therefore I have upon
2525 "me shield and corslet. I will not flee the space
"of a foot from the guardian of the mound: but
"at the rampart it shall be to us two as Fate, the
"lord of every man, decides. I am eager in spirit,
"so that I forbear from boasting against the
"winged fighter.

    "Watch on the barrow, ye warriors in your
2530 "armour, defended by coats of mail, which
"of us two can endure wounds best, after the
"desperate onslaught. That is not your affair,
"nor a possibility for any man, save for me alone,
"to put forth his power against the monster, and
2535 "do heroic deeds. By my valour I will win gold;

"or war, the dread destroyer of life, shall carry
"off your lord!"

(2538–2562) *He advances to the cave and challenges the dragon. The latter comes forth, spewing
flame.*

Then rose the doughty champion by his
shield; bold under his helmet, he went clad in
2540 his war-corslet to beneath the rocky cliffs, and
trusted to his own strength—not such is the
coward's way. Then he, who, excellent in virtues,
had lived through many wars,—the tumult of
battles, when armies dash together,—saw by the
2545 rampart a rocky arch whence burst a stream out
from the mound; hot was the welling of the
flood with deadly fire. He could not any while
endure unscorched the hollow near the hoard,
by reason of the dragon's flame.

2550 Then did the chieftain of the Geats, in his
rage, let a cry burst forth from his breast. Stout-
heartedly he stormed, his voice, distinct in
battle, went ringing under the grey rock. Hate
was enkindled,—the guardian of the hoard dis-
2555 cerned the voice of man. No time was left to
beg for peace.

First came from out the rock the monster's
breath, the hot vapour of battle; the earth resounded. Under the mound the hero, Geatish
2560 lord, raised his shield's disc against the terrible
stranger. Then was the coiled creature's heart
impelled to seek the contest.

(2562–2580) Beowulf draws his sword, and waits
for the dragon's attack. As he comes forward, the king
deals him a blow with his sword, though not such a
mighty one as he wished.

The doughty war-prince had drawn his sword,
an ancient inheritance, very keen of edge; in
2565 each one of the hostile pair was terror at the
other. Stout-heartedly the lord of friends stood
by his upright shield, what time the serpent
quickly coiled itself together; he waited in his
armour. Then, fiery and twisted, he came gliding
2570 towards him—hastening to his fate. The shield
gave its good shelter to the famous chief in life
and limb a shorter time than had his longing
looked for, if he at that time, that first day, was
to command victory in the contest: but Fate
2575 did not thus ordain for him. The Lord of the
Geats swung his hand upwards, struck the
grisly monster with his mighty ancestral weapon,
so that the bright blade gave way on his bone,
and bit less firmly than the warrior-king, driven
to straits, had need.

(2580–2601) The reptile belches forth more
flame, and still the sword fails its owner in his need.
He is seen to be in sore straits by his little company;
but they retreat, panic-stricken, into a neighbouring
wood.

2580   Then was the guardian of the barrow fierce
in spirit after the battle-stroke, and threw out

N

murderous fire; his hostile flames flew far and
wide. The lord and treasure-giver of the Geats
boasted not of glorious victories; the bare war-
2585 weapon, the blade trusty in former times, had
failed him in the fray, as it should not have done.
That was no pleasant journey, that the famous
son of Ecgtheow should have to leave the surface
of this earth and inhabit against his will a
2590 dwelling elsewhere;—for so must every man
give up his transitory days.

Not long was it before the champions met
each other again. The guardian of the hoard
took fresh heart, his breast heaved with his
breathing once again; and he who used to rule
2595 a people suffered anguish, hedged about with
flame. Never a whit did his comrades, those sons
of nobles, stand round him in a body, doing
deeds of warlike prowess; but they shrank back
into the wood and took care of their lives. The
2600 heart of one of them alone surged with regrets,
—in him who is right-thinking nothing can ever
set aside the claims of kinship!

XXXVI

WIGLAF GOES FORWARD TO HELP BEOWULF
IN HIS EXTREMITY. THE KING
RECEIVES A FATAL WOUND

[Lines 2602–2693]

(2602–2610) *One of the company, Wiglaf, calling*

to mind the favours he had had from Beowulf,
is struck with remorse, and prepares to join in the
fray.

He was called Wiglaf, son of Weohstan, a
much loved shield-warrior, a Scylfing prince,
kinsman of Ælfhere. He perceived that his
2605 lord was tortured by the heat under his helmet.
Then he called to mind the favours which he
had bestowed upon him in time past, the rich
dwelling-place of the Wægmundings, and all
power over the people, just as his father had it.
And then he could not forbear; his hand seized
2610 the disc, the yellow linden-shield, and he drew
his ancient sword.

(2611–2625) The history of Wiglaf's sword.
Weohstan, his father, had taken it from Onela's
nephew Eanmund, whom he had slain. He kept it
until his son Wiglaf was grown to man's estate, and
then handed it down to him.

This last was known among men as the
legacy of Eanmund, the son of Ohthere, of
whom, when a friendless exile, Weohstan was
slayer in fight by edge of sword, and bore off to
2615 his kinsmen the burnished helmet, the ring-mail
corslet and the ancient giant-made sword which
Onela had given him—his kinsman's war-
harness, a battle-outfit ready to his hand. Onela
did not speak about the feud, although Weoh-

stan had laid low his brother's son. He kept
2620 these treasures—sword and corslet—many years,
until his son could compass doughty deeds, as his
old father had done. Then when he passed away
from life, full of years, on his journey hence,
he gave to him among the Geats a countless
2625 number of habiliments of war of every kind.

*(2625–2630) This was the first time Wiglaf had
fought by the side of Beowulf; his courage was good
and his sword proved trusty.*

This was the first time that the young champion was to go through the storm of battle
with his noble lord; his courage did not melt
within him, nor did his kinsman's heirloom fail
him in the contest; the serpent found that out,
2630 when they had come together.

*(2631–2660) Before he goes, he rebukes his com-
rades for their ingratitude and cowardice in the hour
of need. For his part, he will share the fortunes of war
with his lord.*

Wiglaf spoke many fitting words (sad was his
soul) and said to his companions: "I remember
"that time at which we drank the mead, how in
2635 "the beer-hall we pledged ourselves to our lord,
"who gave us the rings, that we would repay
"him for the war-equipments, the helmets and
"hard swords, if any need like this befell him. He

"of his own will chose us among the host for
2640 "this adventure, deemed us worthy of honour,
"and gave to me these treasures, because he
"counted us distinguished spear-men, gallant
"warriors beneath our helmets; although he,
"our lord, the shepherd of his people, purposed
"to achieve this deed of bravery by himself, be-
2645 "cause he among men had done the greatest acts
"of heroism, daring deeds. Now has the day
"come, when our liege lord needs the strength
"of noble fighting-men. Let us go to him, and
"help our battle-leader, so long as heat, grim fire-
2650 "horror may be! As for myself, God knows, far
"rather had I that the flame should swallow up
"my body with my generous lord. To me it does
"not seem fitting that we should carry back our
"bucklers to our home, unless we may first fell
2655 "the foe, and shield the life of the lord of the
"Geats.

"Full well I know that this is not what he de-
"serves for his past deeds, that he alone of
"the noble warriors of the Geats should suffer
"affliction,—fall in the fray. To us shall be in
"common sword and helmet, corslet and coat
2660 "of mail."

*(2661–2668) On joining Beowulf, he encourages
him to do his best, and assures him of his help.*

Then he plunged through the deadly fumes;
went helmeted to help his lord; spoke in few

words: "Beloved Beowulf, accomplish all things
"well, just as thou saidst in youthful days of
2665 "yore, that thou wouldst never in thy life leave
"thy glory to fail. Now must thou, resolute chief,
"renowned in deeds, protect thy life with all thy
"might: and I will help thee."

(2669–2693) *The dragon attacks Wiglaf, and
Beowulf drives his sword Nægling into the monster's head; but it snaps, and the dragon gives him
a deadly bite in the neck. The blood gushes out in
torrents.*

2669 After these words, the serpent, the dread
malicious spirit, came angrily a second time,
bright with surging fire, and fell upon his foes,
the loathed mankind. His shield was burnt up to
the boss by waves of fire, his corslet could afford
2675 the youthful spear-warrior no help; but the
young man did valorously under his kinsman's
shield after his own was destroyed by the flames.
Then once more the warlike prince was mindful
of glorious deeds. By main force he struck with
his battle-sword so that it stuck in the head,
2680 driven in by the onslaught. Nægling snapped!
Beowulf's old, grey-hued sword failed him in the
fray. It was not granted him that iron blades
should help him in the fight. The hand was too
2685 strong which, so I have heard, by its stroke over-
strained every sword, when he bore to the fray
a weapon wondrous hard; it was none the better
for him.

Then a third time the people's foe, the dread
fiery dragon, was intent on fighting. He rushed
2690 upon the hero, when occasion favoured him,
hot and fierce in battle, and enclosed his whole
neck between his sharp teeth; he was bathed in
. life-blood—the gore gushed out in streams.

XXXVII

CONTINUATION OF THE FIGHT, AND DEATH OF THE
DRAGON. BEOWULF, DYING OF HIS WOUND,
ASKS TO SEE THE TREASURE

[Lines 2694–2751]

(2694–2711) *Wiglaf wounds the dragon and the
fire from him abates; the king revives for a short time
and cuts the reptile asunder.*

I am told that then in the dire need of the
2695 people's king, the noble warrior stood up and
showed his courage, his skill and daring, as his
nature was. He cared not about the head: but
the brave man's hand was scorched the while he
helped his kinsman, so that he, the man in
2700 armour, struck the vengeful stranger a little
lower down, in such wise that the sword, gleaming and overlaid, plunged in, and the fire began
thenceforth to abate.

Then the king himself once more gained
sway over his senses, drew the keen deadly
knife, sharp in battle, that he wore upon his
2705 corslet, and the protector of the Geats cut

through the serpent in the middle. They had felled the foe: daring had driven out his life, and they, the kindred nobles, had destroyed him. So should a man and chieftain be in time of need! That was for the prince the last of days
2710 of victory by his own deeds,—of work in the world.

(2712–2723) It becomes evident that Beowulf's wound is mortal. Wiglaf bathes it, and undoes his armour.

Then the wound which erewhile the dragon had inflicted on him began to burn and swell; quickly he found out that deadly venom seethed
2715 within his breast,—poison within him.

Then the chieftain wise in thought went on until he sat on a seat by the rampart; he gazed on the work of giants—how the ageless earth-dwelling contained within it vaulted arches, firm
2720 on columns. Then with his hands the thane, exceedingly good, bathed with water the famous prince, blood-stained from the battle, his friend and lord, exhausted by the fight, and undid his helmet.

(2724–2751) Then Beowulf, feeling that death is near, grieves that he has no son to whom he may leave his armour. He comforts himself with the thought of his upright life, and asks Wiglaf to bring the treasure out of the cave, that he may have the last joy of gazing on it.

Beowulf discoursed: despite his hurt, his
2725 grievous deadly wound, he spoke,—he knew
full well that he had used up his time of earthly
joy. Then was his count of days all passed
away, and death immeasurably near: "Now
"should I have wished to give my son my battle-
2730 "garments, if it had been so ordained that
"any heir, issue of my body, should come after
"me. I have ruled over this people fifty winters;
"there was not one of the kings of neighbouring
2735 "tribes who dared encounter me with weapons,
"or could weigh me down with fear. In my
"own home I awaited what the times destined
"for me, kept my own well, did not pick
"treacherous quarrels, nor have I sworn unjustly
2740 "any oaths. In all this may I, sick with deadly
"wounds, have solace; because the Ruler of men
"may never charge me with the murder of
"kinsfolk, when my life parts from my body.

"Now quickly do thou go, beloved Wiglaf,
"and view the hoard under the gray rock, now
2745 "that the serpent lies dead,—sleeps sorely
"wounded and bereft of treasure. Haste now,
"that I may see the ancient wealth, the golden
"store, may well survey the bright and curious
"gems; so that by reason of the wealth of
2750 "treasure I may leave life more calmly and the
"people which I ruled over so long."

XXXVIII

THE LAST WORDS AND DEATH OF BEOWULF

[Lines 2752–2820]

(2752–2766) Wiglaf enters the vault and beholds the treasure, rusted and dull, but of huge value.

Then, I was told, after these words, the son of
Weohstan quickly obeyed his wounded lord,
maimed in fight, and went in his linked armour,
2755 his woven coat of mail, under the barrow's
vault. There, proud in triumph, the brave young
retainer beheld, when he went by the seat,
many a costly ornament—glittering gold lying
on the ground, marvels on the wall, and the
2760 lair of the serpent, the ancient creature who flew
by twilight,—drinking-cups standing, vessels
of bygone races, unpolished and deprived of
their adornments. There was many a helmet,
old and rusty, many an armlet, twisted with
2765 cunning. Treasure, gold in the earth, may easily
get the better of any man, conceal it who will.

(2767–2782) The cavern is lit up by a wondrous gleaming banner, which Wiglaf carries off, together with a load of goblets and dishes.

Moreover, he saw, hanging high above the
hoard, a standard all of gold, greatest of marvels
wrought by hand, woven by human skill. From
2770 this a light shone forth, so that he could discern

the surface of the ground, and scrutinize the treasures. There was no vestige of the serpent, for the sword had destroyed him.

Thus I learnt how in the caverned hill one man rifled the hoard, the old-time work of giants, 2775 and at his own will laid in his bosom drinking-cups and dishes; he took also the standard, brightest of banners. The sword of the aged prince (its blade was iron) had before that wounded him who had long been protector of 2780 the treasures, who had for the hoard put forth his burning terror of flame, at midnight fiercely welling out, till by a violent death he died.

(2783–2793) *He hastens back to Beowulf, fearing that he may not find him alive. He is, indeed, at the last gasp: but after being refreshed with water, is able to make a dying speech.*

The messenger hastened, eager for return, impelled by the treasures. Anxiety tortured him 2785 as to whether he, the brave-minded one, would find the Geats' lord alive in the open place where he had left him, shorn of his strength, erewhile. At last he, bearing the treasures, found the famous prince, his lord, bleeding and at the 2790 end of life. Once more he began to sprinkle him with water, until the beginning of a speech broke forth from the store-house of his mind,—in sorrow the warrior-king spoke, and looked upon the gold.

(2794–2808) Beowulf thanks God that he has been permitted to see the treasure and to have been the means of winning it. He has sacrificed his life in the contest, and he asks that a barrow, to be called Beowulf's barrow, may be raised for a remembrance of him on the cliff.

"I utter in words my thanks to the Ruler of
2795 "all, the King of Glory, the everlasting Lord, for
"the treasures which I here gaze upon, in that
"I have been allowed to win such things for my
"people before my day of death! Now that I
"have given my old life in barter for the hoard
2800 "of treasure, do ye henceforth supply the people's
"needs,—I may stay here no longer.

"Bid the war-veterans raise a splendid barrow
"after the funeral fire, on a projection by the sea,
2805 "which shall tower high on Hronesness as a
"memorial for my people, so that seafarers who
"urge their tall ships from afar over the spray
"of ocean shall thereafter call it Beowulf's
"barrow."

(2809–2816) Then he takes off his collar and gives it to Wiglaf, with his helmet, ring and corslet. He will be the last survivor of the Wægmunding family when Beowulf is no more.

The brave-souled prince undid from off his
2810 neck the golden collar, gave it to the thane, the
young spear-warrior, and his gold-mounted

helmet, ring and corslet,—bade him use them
well. "Thou art the last of our race, the Wæg-
2815 "mundings. Fate has swept off all my kinsfolk,
"undaunted nobles, to their doom. I must go
"after them."

*(2817–2820) After these words, Beowulf's soul
takes its departure.*

That was the veteran's last expression of his
spirit's thoughts before the funeral pyre was his
lot,—the hot destructive flames. His soul
2820 departed from his body to journey to the doom
of righteous men.

XXXIX

BEOWULF'S COWARDLY FOLLOWERS COME OUT
OF THE WOOD, AND WIGLAF AGAIN RE-
PROACHES THEM AND FORESHADOWS
THEIR PUNISHMENT

[Lines 2821–2891]

*(2821–2845) It was a sad day for Wiglaf. True,
the dragon was stopped for ever of his mischief:
but the beloved king had paid for victory with his
life.*

So it went hardly with the younger man, that
he beheld the most beloved on the ground,
suffering miserably at the end of life. His
2825 destroyer, the terrible cave-dragon, lay, also,

bereft of life, overwhelmed by ruin. No longer
might the coiled serpent have power over the
hoard of treasures. But iron blades, the hard,
battle-dinted result of forging, had destroyed
2830 him: so that he who could fly far and wide had
fallen motionless from his wounds upon the
ground, hard by his treasure-house. Not at all
did he whirl flying through the air at midnight
and show himself, proud of his rich treasures;
2835 but on the earth he fell by the war-prince's
power of hand.

So far as I have heard, indeed, no man of
might, daring though he might be in every sort
of deed, could prevail to rush against the
2840 venomous foe's blast, or ransack with his hands
the hall of rings, if on the mount he found the
guardian watching.

By Beowulf the mass of the splendid treasures
was paid for with death; both had travelled to
the end of fitful life.

(2845–2859) *The ten cowards come out of the
wood and gaze on Wiglaf and the dead body of the
king.*

2845   Not long after was it that the laggards in
battle left the wood, ten cowardly traitors
together, who had shrunk from wielding their
spears in their lord's great need. But in shame
2850 they bore their shields, their war-harness, to
where the old chief lay, and gazed on Wiglaf.

This warrior sat exhausted by the shoulders of
his lord, and tried to rally him with water,—
but it availed him nothing. He could not keep
2855 on earth the chieftain's spirit, much though he
wished it, nor alter anything ordained by the
Almighty. For men of all degrees God's judgment ruled their deeds, just as it still does now.

*(2860–2883) Wiglaf reproaches the recreants.
They have proved themselves unworthy of the armour
they wear and the presents they have had from their
lord. Beowulf had managed to quell the dragon
single-handed, with such slight but willing help as
Wiglaf could give him.*

2860　　Then a severe retort came promptly from the
youthful hero for such as had lacked courage.
Wiglaf, the son of Weohstan, spoke out, the
man, sick at heart, looked on the hated ones:
2865 "Lo! this can he say who wills to speak the
"truth;—that the lord of men who gave you
"those costly things, the war-harness that you
"stand there in, when the chieftain gave many a
"time on his ale-bench helmets and corslets,
"the trustiest he could find far or near to
2870 "his thanes sitting in hall—(that he) completely
"threw away that armour,—woefully, when
"war befell him. No reason had the king to
"boast about his comrades in the field; yet God,
"master of victories, granted him that single-
2875 "handed he might avenge himself with the

"sword, when prowess was needed of him.
"Poorly was I able to act as body-guard for
"him in the fight; and yet I made a start beyond
"my power to help my kinsman. When with the
2880 "sword I struck the deadly foe, he ever was the
"weaker,—the fire welled forth less strongly
"from his head. Too few defenders thronged
"around the prince, when the time of hardship
"came upon him."

(*2884–2891*) *He foreshadows their miserable fate.*

"Now shall the receiving of treasure and gifts
2885 "of swords, all joy of ownership, and comfort be
"wanting to your race; each man of your family
"will have to wander, shorn of his landed posses-
"sions, as soon as nobles far and wide hear of
2890 "your flight, your despicable act! Better is death
"to every one of noble birth than an inglorious
"life."

XL

THE MESSENGER'S REPORT. HE SPECULATES ON
THE RESULT OF THE DEATH, IN A
HISTORICAL RETROSPECT

[Lines 2892–2945]

(*2892–2910*) *Wiglaf sends one of the company
back to the stronghold with the sad news, who reports
it faithfully; how Beowulf and the dragon are dead
and Wiglaf keeps guard by the king's body.*

Then he bade the battle-deed be told in the stronghold, up over the sea-cliff, where, depressed in spirit, the whole forenoon the band of noble warriors remained, the shield-bearers, 2895 in suspense about two things—his death-day and the return of the dear man.

Little did he who rode up to the headland keep back of the latest tidings,—he told it faith- 2900 fully in the hearing of all: "Now lies the joy- "giver and lord of the Geat people still on his "death-bed,—sleeps through the dragon's deeds "in slaughterous rest. His deadly enemy lies "side by side with him, laid low by knife- "wounds,—himself could not with a sword in- 2905 "flict a wound in any way upon the monster. "Wiglaf, the son of Weohstan, sits by Beowulf, "the living noble by the dead; he stands guard "over the head of friend and foe with weariness "of heart."

(2910–2921) *The messenger fears that when Beowulf's death is common knowledge, there will be trouble with the Franks and Frisians. The Merovingian dynasty has never been really friendly with the Geats since Hygelac's raid into Friesland.*

2910   "Now there is likelihood for the people of a "time of warfare, as soon as the king's fall "becomes widely known among the Franks and "Frisians. Hard fighting was purposed against "the Hugas, when Hygelac came journeying

o

2915 "with his ships of war to Frisian land, where
"the Hetware vanquished him in battle, and
"bravely brought to pass by their superior
"strength that he, the armoured chieftain, had
"to yield. He fell among his followers,—not an
2920 "ornament did that prince give to his noble
"warriors. Even since that, the favour of the
"Merovingian king has been denied to us."

EPISODE OF THE BATTLE OF RAVENSWOOD AND
DEATH OF ONGENTHEOW

*(2922–2945) Probably there will be an attack
by the Swedes also. The Swedish King Ongentheow
killed Hæthcyn at Ravenswood and avenged the
seizure of his queen; but after his victory Hygelac
bore down on him with the flower of his army.*

"Nor do I in the least expect peace or fair
"dealing from the Swedish people; for it is widely
2925 "known that Ongentheow deprived Hæthcyn, the
"son of Hrethel, of his life near Ravenswood, when
"the Geatish people first arrogantly attacked the
"warlike Scylfings. Quickly did the veteran father
"of Ohthere, old and terrible, give him a return
2930 "blow, killed the sea-king (Hæthcyn) and, though
"an old man, rescued his wife, the mother of Onel
"and Ohthere, bereft of her gold adornments; and
"then he followed his deadly enemies until with
"difficulty they escaped to Ravenswood without
2935 "their lord. Then with a mighty army he encom
"passed those whom the sword had not despatched
"faint from their wounds, and through the livelong

"night he often threatened the wretched band with
"misery—said he would destroy them by morn
2940 "with edge of sword—hang some on gallows-trees
"as sport for birds. Once more came help to the
"sad-hearted ones with early dawn, when they
"were ware of Hygelac's horn, his trumpet
"blast,—when the hero came, bearing down on
2945 "their track with a picked body of his troops."

XLI

THE MESSENGER FINISHES HIS RETROSPECT. THE WHOLE ARMY GOES TO SEE THE PLACE OF THE ENCOUNTER AND THE DEAD KING

[Lines 2946–3057]

*(2946–2960) Ongentheow retreated to a fast-
ness, but was brought to bay by Hygelac and killed
by Eofor.*

"The bloody track of Swedes and Geats, the
"murderous strife of men, was visible far and
"wide,—how these peoples fostered the feud
"between themselves. Then the brave king, the
"care-worn veteran, went with his tribesmen to
2950 "his fastness. The lord Ongentheow moved further
"off. He had had knowledge of Hygelac's fighting
"powers, of the proud one's skill in war, and
"trusted not in resistance that he might withstand
"the sea-folk and defend his treasures, children and
2955 "wife from the ocean-farers : and so after that the
"aged man retreated from thence once more behind
"an earth-wall. Then was chase given to the
"Swedish folk, the banners of Hygelac overran the

2960   "fastness until Hygelac's retainers pressed on to the
        "enclosure."

        *(2961–2981) His death happened in this wise:
        Wulf (Eofor's brother) engaged in a hand-to-hand
        combat with him, but was nearly killed by a desperate
        stroke on the head from the king's sword. Then
        Eofor dealt him (Ongentheow) a fatal blow.*

        "There was the grey-haired Ongentheow driven
        "to bay by the edges of swords, so that the people's
        "king had to submit to his end at the hands of Eofor
2965   "alone. Angrily did Wulf the son of Wonred strike
        "at him with his weapon, so that at the stroke
        "the blood spurted forth from the veins under his
        "hair. Yet was the veteran Scylfing not afraid, but
        "quickly paid the deadly blow back with a harder
2970   "counter-stroke, as soon as he, the people's king,
        "had turned on him. The active son of Wonred
        "could not give the return blow to the older man:
        "but Ongentheow first clave Wulf's helmet on
        "his head, so that he was forced to sink down,
2975   "stained with blood. He fell to earth; and still he
        "was not doomed, but he came round, though the
        "wound pained him.

        "Hygelac's sturdy follower (Eofor) broke his
        "broad blade, his sword made by giants of old,
2980   "over the protecting shield, the massive helmet,
        "the while his brother lay dead; and then the
        "king fell down,—the shepherd of his folk was
        "wounded mortally."

        *(2982–2998) Eofor strips Ongentheow of his
        armour and takes the spoil to Hygelac, who requites*

him and his brother Wulf with rich presents and
land, and gives Eofor his only daughter in marriage.

"Then were there many who bandaged his
"brother Wulf and raised him up quickly, when
"victory in the battle-field had been granted them.
2985   "Meanwhile one warrior stripped the other, and
"took from Ongentheow his iron corslet, his strong
"and hilted sword and his helmet,—bore to
"Hygelac the veteran's harness. And he received
"the spoils and honourably promised him rewards
2990   "among men; and he performed it too,—he, lord
"of the Geats and son of Hrethel, recompensed
"Wulf and Eofor for the storm of battle with
"copious treasure when he had got back home;
"and gave to each of them a hundred thousand
"(sceattas) in land and linked rings. No man on
2995   "earth could blame him for the gifts, since they
"had earned the honours by fighting,—and to
"Eofor he gave his only daughter as a pledge of
"favour, and to grace his home."

(2999–3007) *Looking to the above history, the*
messenger expects an attack from the Swedes directly
they hear of Beowulf's death.

3000   "That is the feud and enmity, the deadly
"hatred of men, according to which the people
"of the Swedes will attack us, as I have no
"doubt, when they learn that our lord is dead.
"It was he who in the past guarded against
3005   "enemies our wealth and kingdom—the bold
"shield-warriors after the fall of mighty men—

"advanced the people's welfare and furthermore
"did deeds of valour."

*(3007–3030) Let us all go, said he, to take a last
look at the king, and then bring him to the funeral
pyre. Heaps of blood-bought treasure shall be consumed with him. Now the great captain has gone,
many a fair maiden will be carried off into foreign
lands, and the raven will gloat over the slain after
many a fight.*

"Now speed is best, that we should look upon
"the people's king there, and bring him who gave
3010 "us treasures on his way to the funeral pyre.
"Not one part only shall be consumed with the
"bold warrior; for there is a hoard of treasures,
"countless gold, acquired at terrible cost, and
"now at last rings bought with his own life. These
3015 "shall the fire eat up, the flames consume. No
"noble shall wear an ornament in his memory,
"nor shall fair maiden have a torque-adornment
"round her neck; but sad of mood, bereft of gold,
"they shall tread the land of exile—often, not
3020 "merely once,—now that the army-leader has
"laid aside laughter, joy and mirth. Therefore
"shall many a spear, chill at morn, be grasped
"with fingers, lifted by the hand: no sound of
"harp shall wake the warriors, but the dark
3025 "raven, eager after doomed men, shall recount
"many things, and tell the eagle how it sped him
"at the feast, when he, contending with the wolf,
"laid bare the slain."

Thus the brave youth was a teller of grievous
3030 tales: nor was he much amiss in facts or words.

*(3030–3057) The whole company go mourning
to the scene of the dread contest, and there behold
their warrior-king, and by him the dead dragon and
the ancient treasures. To Beowulf had God granted
to break the spell which hedged the riches round!*

The whole band rose; they went sadly, with
welling tears, by Earnanæs to see the wondrous
sight. There they found on the sand, lifeless,
keeping his bed of rest, him who in times past
3035 gave them rings. There had the hero's last day
come to pass, in which the warrior-king, the
Geat's prince, had died his wondrous death.
But first they saw a stranger being there, the
hateful serpent, lying on the plain there oppo-
3040 site. The fiery dragon, terribly bright, was
scorched with glowing embers. Fifty measured
feet long was it as it lay. Sometimes by night it
used to dwell in the joyous air; then it came down
3045 again to seek its den;—and there it was, rigid in
death. It had inhabited the last of its earth-caves.
Goblets and flagons stood by it, dishes lay there
and precious swords, rusty and eaten through,
3050 as if they had lodged there a thousand winters in
earth's bosom. At that time the mighty heritage,
the gold store of men of old, was hedged round
with a spell, that no man might touch the
treasure-chamber, had not God himself, true

3055 king of victories (he is the shield of men),
granted to whom he would to open the hoard,
even to such a man as seemed meet to him.

XLII

REFLECTIONS ON THE INSCRUTABILITY OF FATE.
PREPARATIONS FOR THE FUNERAL

[Lines 3058–3136]

(*3058–3075*) *The future is shrouded in mystery.
This adventure was the death of Beowulf;—and yet
he was not greedy after gold.*

Then it was manifest that the way of him who
had unrighteously concealed the treasure under
3060 the rock-wall had not prospered. The guardian
had at first killed off a very great man; and then
the feud was savagely avenged. It is ever a
mystery in what place a noble of brave repute
may have to meet his fortune's end,—when the
3065 man may dwell no longer in the mead-hall with
his kinsmen. With Beowulf thus it was, when
he sought out the guardian of the mound, and
deadly conflicts—he knew not for what reason
his parting from the world should happen. The
3070 great chiefs who put that treasure there had
laid on it a deep curse until doomsday, so that
the man who should plunder that place should
be guilty of sin, be shut up in devil's haunts,
bound in hell-bonds and tormented grievously.
Yet by no means too eagerly had Beowulf before

3075 gazed upon its owner's treasure of gold with the curse on it.

(3076–3100) Wiglaf again laments the calamity which has fallen upon the people. He speaks of the old king's last moments, and of his wish that a notable barrow should be erected in his memory.

Wiglaf, son of Weohstan, spoke:—"Often "must many a noble suffer misery through the "will of one, as it has happened to us. We could
3080 "not give any counsel to the dear prince, the "guardian of his kingdom,—that he should not "attack the keeper of the gold, but let him lie "where he had long time been,—rest in his "dwelling till the world's end. He held fast "to his high destiny! The hoard is open to
3085 "view, terribly acquired. Too cruel was the "fate that drove thither the people's king. I "was within, and scanned it all,—the treasures "of the chamber,—when it was granted me; "not by any means was the journey under the
3090 "earth-wall allowed me in friendly wise. I "grasped hastily with my hands a great o'er- "whelming load of hoarded treasures,—bore "it out thither to my king: he was then still "alive, conscious and sound in mind. The old man
3095 "said many things in his distress,—told me to "greet you, bade you build, according to your "champion's deeds, a lofty barrow in the place "of the funeral pyre, great and magnificent, for "that he was of men on the wide earth the

3100 "worthiest warrior so long as he was suffered to
"enjoy the riches of his stronghold."

*(3101–3109) He invites the company to have a
last look at the heap of treasures, while a bier is being
got ready for the king's body.*

"Come now and let us haste to see and visit
"once more the heap of cunning treasures, a
"wondrous sight under the wall of rock! I will
3105 "guide you, that you may see the rings and thick
"gold near enough. Let the bier be quickly made
"ready when we come out, and then let us carry
"our lord, the beloved man, to where he shall
"wait long in the keeping of the Almighty."

*(3110–3119) He obtains wood from the neigh-
bouring notables, wherewith to kindle the funeral pyre
of the great warrior-chief who had taken part in so
many battles.*

3110   Then Weohstan's son, the hero bold in battle,
bade orders be given to many men of rank, that
the leaders of the people should fetch wood
for the pyre from far to place by the brave
chief: "The dark flame towers high—now shall
3115 "fire consume the strong support of warriors,
"who often braved the shower of darts, when a
"storm of arrows, forced from the strings,
"quivered above the wall of shields; when the
"shaft did its office, and urged forth the barb,
"sped by its feather-gear."

(3120–3136) Seven thanes are chosen out to carry away the treasures from the cave. They push the dragon over the cliff and load a wagon with the valuables. The body of Beowulf is also borne away to the promontory on which the funeral fire is to be lit.

3120   And so the wise son of Weohstan called from out the band the picked thanes of the king, seven all told—and he with those seven warriors went under the foeman's vault; one who went in front,
3125 bore in his hand a flaming torch. Who should then spoil the hoard was not arranged by lot, as soon as the warriors saw any part of it remain unguarded in the chamber and lie perishing;
3130 little did any grieve that hurriedly they should carry off the costly treasures. Also they pushed the dragon, the serpent, over the cliff,—let the waves take the guardian of the treasure, the flood enfold him. There was an altogether countless store of twisted gold loaded upon a
3135 wagon; and the prince, the ancient warrior, was borne away to Hronesness.

XLIII

THE FUNERAL OF BEOWULF

[Lines 3137–3182]

(3137–3155) The Geats make a funeral pyre, placing the body of their lord in the midst of a heap

of armour, and set fire to it. The roaring of the
flames mingles with the weeping of the people.

The people of the Geats then made ready for
him on the ground a firm-built funeral pyre,
hung round with helmets, battle-shields, bright
3140 corslets, as he had begged them to do. Then
mighty men, lamenting, laid in its midst the
famous prince, their beloved lord. The warriors
then began to kindle on the mount the greatest
of funeral pyres; the dark wood-smoke towered
3145 above the blazing mass; the roaring flame
mingled with the noise of weeping—the raging
of the winds had ceased—till it had crumbled
up the body, hot to its core. Depressed in soul,
they uttered forth their misery, and mourned
3150 their lord's death. Moreover, the Geatish woman
with hair bound up, sang in memory of Beowulf
a doleful dirge and said repeatedly that she
greatly feared evil days for herself, much carnage,
3155 the terror of the foe, humiliation and captivity.
Heaven swallowed up the smoke.

(3156–3168) Then they constructed a barrow,
covering in the remains, and in it they placed the
riches they had taken from the hoard.

Then people of the Geats raised a mound upon
the cliff, which was high and broad and visible
from far by voyagers on sea: and in ten days they
built the beacon of the warrior bold in battle.

3160   The remnant of the burning they begirt with
a wall in such sort as skilled men could plan
most worthy of him. In the barrow they placed
collars and brooches—all such adornments as
3165   brave-minded men had before taken from the
hoard. They left the wealth of nobles to the
earth to keep,—left the gold in the ground,
where it still exists, as unprofitable to men as it
had been before.

(*3169–3182*) *Twelve chieftains ride round the
barrow, lamenting their king in a dirge and praising
him for his manliness, his mildness and his longing
to be worthy of men's praise.*

Then the warriors brave in battle, sons of
3170   nobles, twelve in all, rode round the barrow ; they
would lament their loss, mourn for their king,
utter a dirge, and speak about their hero. They
reverenced his manliness, extolled highly his deeds
3175   of valour ;—so it is meet that man should praise
his friend and lord in words, and cherish him in
heart when he must needs be led forth from the
body.
Thus did the people of the Geats, his hearth-
companions, mourn the death of their lord,
3180   and said that he had been of earthly kings the
mildest and the gentlest of men, the kindest to
his people and the most eager for fame.

THE FINNESBURG FRAGMENT

A. PROSE TRANSLATION

". . . GABLES are burning!" Then spake Hnaef,
the king young in war—"This is no dawning
"from the east, nor here does any dragon fly,
"nor here do this hall's gables burn, but hither
5 "they bear forth (weapons), the birds (of battle)
"sing, the grey-coated wolf howls, there is din of
"spear, shield answers to shaft. Now shines this
"errant moon beneath the clouds. Now begin evil
"deeds, which will further this enmity of the
10 "people. But wake ye now, my warriors, hold fast
"your shields, think of brave deeds, rush forward
"in the van, be stout of heart!"

Then arose many a thane, bedight with gold,
and girded on his sword. Then to the door two
15 noble warriors went, Sigeferth and Eaha, and
drew their swords, and at the other door Ordlaf
and Guthlaf; and Hengest himself turned him
upon their track. Moreover, Garulf exhorted
20 Guthhere, that he should not at the first onset
go in his armour to the doors of the hall,—(risk)
so precious a life, now that the man hardy in
battle purposed to take it; but the valiant warrior,
asked clearly over all, who held the door?

"Sigeferth is my name," quoth he, "I am
25 "prince of the Secgan, a well-known rover. Many
"troubles, hard conflicts, have I passed through;

178

"here is ordained for thee whatever thou thyself
"dost seek from me."

30 Then at the wall rose the din of battle; the
vaulted shield, protector of the body, was like
to come apart in heroes' hands. The floor of the
stronghold resounded, till in the fight Garulf
lay dead, Guthlaf's son, foremost of those dwelling
in the land, and by him many heroes. A crowd
of foemen fell pale in death; the raven hovered,
35 dark and sallow-brown; the gleam of swords shone,
as if all Finnesburg were on fire. Never have I
heard tell in mortal strife of sixty conquering
fighters bearing themselves better and more
worthily, nor ever men pay better for the shining
mead than did his liegemen yield return to Hnaef.
40 Five days they fought, and not one of their followers fell, but they held the doors. Then did the
wounded chief retire and went away,—said that
his coat of mail was broken through, his armour
45 unavailing, and moreover his helmet pierced.

Then straightway the guardian of the people
asked him how the warriors got over their wounds,
or which of the youths . . .

B. Verse Translation

". . . Gables burning!"
Said king Hnaef then, young in battle—
"This dawns not from the east; no dragon hither
flies,
"Nor do the gables burn here in this hall of ours.

"But hither forth they fare, the birds of battle
    sing,
"The grey-coat howls, the war-wood clanks,
"Shield answers shaft. Now shines the moon
"Fitful through cloud. Sad work's on foot
"To bring about this people's bale!
"But wake ye now, my fighting-men,
"Hold fast your shields, cherish brave thoughts,
"Rush to the front, be stout of heart!"

Then from his rest rose many a thane
Bedight with gold,—girt on his sword.

Then to the door there went those valiant fighters
    twain
Eaha, Sigeferth, who drew their battle swords,
And at the other door, Ordlaf and Guthlaf too,
Yea, Hengest's very self, who followed in their
    track.

Then too spake Guthere and begged of Garulf
That he would not at first risk so precious a life
In harness of war at the doors of the hall
Now the hardy-in-fight wished to take it away.

But he openly asked, in the presence of all—
The warrior bold—*Who* was holding the door?
"Sigeferth is my name. I am chief of the Secgs,
"—A hero of mark. Adventures great store
"And hard fights have I had. For thee is ordained
"Whatsoever of ill thou hast purposed for me!"

Then was heard in the hall a slaughterous din,
The warriors' shield in the hands of the brave
—The limb-screen—did sunder, the hall timbers
    dinned,
  Till in the struggle Garulf perished
  First of all that country's dwellers—
  Guthlaf's son—with many good men.

  Pale foemen lay; the raven hovered
  Swarthy, dark-brown; gleamed forth sword-
    flash
  Like as all Finnesburg were a-flaming.

Never have I heard tell that three-score fighting
    men
In any mortal strife bore them in nobler wise,
Or swains the shining mead earned harder any-
    where
Than did his body-guard pay in return to Hnaef.

  They fought five days, and yet there fell
  No brave; but still they held the doors.

Then did a wounded chief retire and gat him gone
—Said that his coat of mail asunder had been
    rent
—His trusty battle-sark—his helmet pierced, as
    well.
Him thereupon he asked (the shepherd of his folk)
What speed the warriors had in healing of their
    wounds
Or whether of the youths . . .

P

NOTES

The text translated is that of Fr. Klaeber, in his *Beowulf and the Fight at Finnsburg*, third edition revised with supplement (D. C. Heath & Co., 1941). These notes deal mainly with passages in which Klaeber's readings have not been accepted and with passages that present special difficulties or points of interest. His edition contains a full *apparatus* of every kind.

Other books which the student will find of special value are:

> *Beowulf*, edited by A. J. Wyatt, revised by R. W. Chambers. (Cambridge, 1914.)
>
> *Beowulf, an Introduction to the Study of the Poem*, etc., by R. W. Chambers; second edition. (Cambridge, 1932.)
>
> *Kommentar zum Beowulf*, by Johannes Hoops. (Heidelberg, 1932.)
>
> *Beowulf and the Seventh Century*, by Ritchie Girvan. (Methuen, 1935.)
>
> *Beowulf, the Monsters and the Critics*, by J. R. R. Tolkien. (British Academy Lecture, 1936.)
>
> The Heyne-Schücking *Beowulf*, 15th ed. re-edited by Else von Schaubert. (Paderborn, 1940.)
>
> *The Rhythms of Beowulf*, by J. C. Pope. (Yale University Press, 1942.)

[The line numbers are those of the Old English text as in Klaeber's third edition, cited as *Klaeber*.]

L. 6. *egsode eorl[as]*: Here, as always where not otherwise indicated, Klaeber's emended text has been accepted. The suggestion of Sewell (*Times Lit. Sup.*, September 11, 1924) that here is a reference to the Heruli, who were in fact conquered by the Danes, may seem attractive; but it has been thought convenient only to depart from Klaeber's views when they are definitely found to be unacceptable.

20. *gode* is here properly the instrumental case of the noun, since the neut. of the adj. may be a noun. The meaning is then "by virtue," that is "by his good deeds"; and *gode* is parallel to *fromum feohgiftum* in the next line.

30–31. *þenden wordum weold . . . lange ahte*. The awkwardness of leaving the verb *ahte* without an expressed object, could be avoided by assuming *ahte* to be a form of *æhte* (gen. or dat.) governed by the verb *weold*. Other examples of *ahte* for *æhte* in Late O.E. and Early M.E. are extant; and *æht*, which usually means "possession," might have the contextual sense of "realm." Then the passage could be translated: "so long as the loved lord of the Scyldings, the dear ruler of the land, held sway over his realm" (*lange* being taken with *þenden*). Or if *weold* could be supposed to take an accusative, *lange* might be an adj. qualifying *ahte*, and *lange ahte* mean "far-flung possessions." But the orthodox view has been retained in the translation.

62. *Hyrde ic þæt* [. . . *wæs On*]*elan cwen:* Klaeber is again accepted for the defective MS. text; and as no woman's name can be found to fit metrical and historical requirements, the name of the fourth child must be left blank.

73. *butan folcscare: folcscaru,* "the people's portion," is originally the common land belonging to each village or community in Germanic times, upon which the inhabitants had the inalienable right to graze their cattle. This survives in the commons which are still to some extent the legal right of the English people.

81–85. *Sele hlifade . . . wæcnan scolde:* This reference to the feud between Hrothgar's son-in-law and the Danish king's family refers to the famous fight between Ingeld the prince of the Heathobards, and the Danish royal family into which he had married by wedding Hrothgar's daughter Freawaru: and the poet takes the burning of Heorot to have been a result of this feud, though later sources would connect this disaster with Hrothgar's nephew Hrothulf who also attacked the king, his benefactor's family and realm. Now as the audience are thoroughly familiar with all the Danish happenings, there is here a kind of tragic irony in this anticipation of the ruin of Heorot at the time of describing its glories (cf. similar anticipations of disaster known to the audience at ll. 781–782 and 1017–1019).

106–107. *forscrifen hæfde. In Caines cynne:* The sentence is taken, as by Chambers, to end with *forscrifen hæfde.* A fresh sentence thus begins with *In,* and no punctuation is placed after *cynne.*

112. *Orcneas:* "evil spirits" does not bring out all the meaning. *Orcneas* is compounded of *orc* (from the Lat. *orcus* "the underworld" or Hades) and *neas* "corpses." Necromancy was practised among the ancient Germani, and was familiar among the pagan Norsemen who revived it in England when they invaded. By this art the newly-buried dead bodies could be made to call up the spirits which had inhabited them: but of course this could, from an early Christian point of view, only be done if such spirits had been evil. *Orcneas,* then, were the evil spirits which could be conjured up from the lower world by means of necromancy.

140. *Bed æfter būrum*: Properly the *buras* were small private rooms or small separate dwellings, belonging to the king and some of the highest chiefs. These *būras* could be reached from the courtyard surrounding the hall, and also by some kind of communicating passage from it (cf. 1310). So great was the terror of Grendel that all discipline and respect broke down, and men sought refuge in the private rooms or dwellings of the aristocracy instead of remaining in the hall as was proper.

154-158. *Sibbe nc wolde . . . to banan folmum*: Grendel did not want peace, which he could only have had by paying up the *wergild* of the thirty of Hrothgar's men he had slain: he would neither stop his murders nor settle the blood-feud by paying compensation: nor was there any need (said with grim irony) to look for a handsome reparation (*bōt* is properly the legal term for the *wergild* or compensation for a life, which the ancient Germanic law required).

168-169. *No he . . . myne wisse*: This awkward passage has not been satisfactorily explained (see Klaeber). It may well be an interpolated statement about Cain, originally intended by a redactor to follow line 110. The Throne is then God's. The phrase *myne witan* (cf. *The Wanderer*, l. 27) seems to mean "to feel love." The meaning may well be that Grendel "could not approach God's throne, that precious thing (maþðum), in the Creator's presence (*for Metode*), nor did he feel His love."

225. *Wedera leode*: The *Geats*, whose name etymologically probably meant *pourers* (of libations) or *sacrificers*, could be called *Weder-Geatas* in poetry if the metre required a longer strongly stressed word with alliterating *w*. This compound had lost by the days of the *Beowulf* poet its original sense of "sacrificers to the storm-god," and merely meant Geats. Hence it was also possible for the poet to use the shortened *Wederas* as here for Geats if the metre needed it, as the etymological sense was not consciously perceived. Similarly the Goths (O.E. *Gotan*) are called *Hreð-Gotan* in Cynewulf's *Elene*: for *hreð* perhaps meant "storm" and the etymological sense of *Gotan* was "sacrificers" (*Gotan* and *Geatas* being forms of the same verbal root with differing grade of vowel, as may be seen by comparing the principal parts of O.E. *geotan* "to pour"). This reminds us that the language of the poem was already in some respects probably a little archaic when it was first recited, as is natural in an aristocratic traditional type of diction. Woden or Odin is first heard of among the peoples of S. Scandinavia from whence both Geats and Goths had come; and from the etymological connections of *Woden* (cf. Latin *ventus*) it seems that he was originally a nature-god of the storm.

298–299. *to Wedermearce. Godfremmendra swylcum:* The sentence is assumed to end with *Wedermearce.* Then *swylcum* is dat. sing., has its usual meaning, and refers to Beowulf. But most editors put a comma after *Wedermearce;* so that *godfremmendra swylcum* will mean "to whomsoever of the noble warriors."

305–306. *ferhwearde heold guþmod grimmon:* MS. *guþmod grummon* can perhaps be defended, by taking *guþmod* as a pl. noun = "battle-hearts" and *grummon* as pret. pl. of *grimman* "rage." Then one might freely render "The hearts of the warriors were filled with excitement." But Klaeber is in accord with most recent scholarship in making the slight emendation of *grummon* to *grimmon* (dat. pl. of adj. *grimm*). As an auspicious animal, the boar might well guard the warriors. But it would be better to take MS. *ferhwearde,* which has a half-space between *ferh* and *wearde,* as separate words. *Ferh* = "boar" (W.S. *fearh*), qualified by the adj. *guþmod;* and this has been done in the translation. Yet one cannot be sure that *ferh* could be used in poetry for "boar," like *swin,* as otherwise it stands for the domestic pig. *Swin* has both uses.

320. *stanfāh:* lit. "adorned with stone," and hence apparently a reference to Roman paving. The poet, making his poem of Denmark, where there would be no such Roman remains, is unconsciously thinking of England, where some Roman roads were still showing relics of Roman paving in his time (cf. 725).

338–339. *Wen' ic þæt ge . . . Hroðgar sohton:* The two obvious reasons for a Germanic prince to seek foreign parts were either adventure or the having been sent into exile : and Wulfgar courteously makes clear that he assumes the former and more honourable one. Added point is given to his remarks when we notice that he himself, as a "prince of the Vandals" (v. 348) had probably come to Hrothgar's service through banishment.

414. MS. *hador,* accepted by Klaeber, should mean "brightness," and hence possibly "firmament" (adj. as noun). But confusion of *d* and *ð* is frequent in this MS., and the emendation *haðor* has been assumed in the translation.

445–451. *Na þu minne þearft . . . leng sorgian:* The point here is that it was the sacred duty of a chieftain's nearest relatives to provide for his funeral rites so that he might have his treasures and weapons etc. in the next life : and since Beowulf would have been slain far from his own country, it would be the duty of Hrothgar (to whose *comitatus* he now belonged) to provide for these. But, he says, with characteristic Germanic humour, there will be no corpse to bury, since Grendel will have eaten it. *Hafelan hydan* (446) seems to refer to the fact that the faces of corpses were covered in burial, as ancient Germanic grave-finds have suggested. *feorme* (451) must mean "disposal" rather than "sustenance" as has been supposed. *Feorm* means "use" in King Alfred's translation of the *Cura Pastoralis* (Preface), for instance ; and we should assume a contextual sense of "disposal" in the phrase *lices feorme*. It would be a poor compliment to Hrothgar if Beowulf were merely telling him that his death would relieve him of the necessity of providing food for the guests.

457. The translation follows Klaeber's decision (in his Supplementary Notes) to accept Grundtvig's century-old proposal to read *For werefyhtum* "for defensive war," because the MS. *fere fyhtum* can best be accounted for with a mere miswriting of an *f* for a *w*. Certainly too this reading makes much better sense in the context.

489–490. MS. *on sæl meoto sige hreð secg*. It seems probable, from the general context and from 496, that Beowulf is being invited to listen, after the banquet, to the *scop;* so that Klaeber's view and that of most editors that *onsæl* is an imperative and *meoto* a noun must be doubted. Moreover, the last two letters of *secgum*, read by nearly all scholars, cannot now be seen in the MS. which is damaged at its margin. The translation takes *sæl* as a noun = "season" and emends *meoto* to *meota* (imperative of *meotian* = W.S. *metian*), when it becomes probable that the missing part of MS. *secg* must be the gen. pl. ending *a.* Scribal *meoto* for *meota* would be a simple dittography.

572–573. *Wyrd oft nereð . . . ellen deah:* Here the pagan fatalism and the Christian idea of a free will which is yet foreknown of God in its results, seem to blend. A man may be saved by his valour by *wyrd* (here fate and God are almost identified), but only provided that he was not already *fæge* "doomed." Early glimmerings, perhaps, of the great medieval problem of predestination and free will. Cf. 2291–2293.

600. MS. *swefeð ond sendeþ:* The attractive conjecture *snedeþ* for *sendeþ*, adopted by Klaeber, would give the meaning "feasts" : but the translation has followed the MS., though the sense of *sendeþ* must remain hypothetical. *Sendeþ* may mean "sends (to death)," or one may compare the O.N. *senda* "offer in sacrifice," or one may conjecture (from the fact that the MS. does not here abbreviate *ond*) a verb *ondsendeþ*, before which a conjunction *ond* has fallen out by haplography. Klaeber (in his Supplementary Notes) reverts to the MS. reading.

725. *On fagne flor:* That this refers to remains of Roman tessellated pavement is suggested by the place-name Fawler
(Berks.) which is called *fag flor* in O.E. charters, and where
tessellated paving was found in 1865. The Germanic invaders may have at times built their halls where Romano-
British buildings had once stood. Several other references to
fag flor occur in O.E. boundary-charters.

769. *ealuscerwen:* the exact meaning of this word is unknown, but
it seems to contain in its first element an already obsolete
word *ealu* with the sense of "good fortune," parallel to the
O.N. Runic inscriptions' *alu* and the written Norse *ǫl.*
Both in O.E. and O.N. these forms were homophones
which might mean "ale" or "good fortune": but in O.E.
the latter had become obsolete and could only have been
used in a traditional compound (*ealuscerwen*) where the
general sense was apprehended by the audience, though
the exact sense of *ealu* was lost (cf. *regnheard* of 326 and
scurheard of 1033). Then the poet of *Andreas* (1528) used
the word *meoduscerwen* with the same general sense of
"disaster," supposing that *ealu* meant "ale" and that he
might change his drink for the alliteration. If *scerwen*
could bear the sense of "scattering," the word *ealuscerwen*
might mean "reversal of good fortune" (*ealu*), and so
"disaster." Klaeber (Supplem. Notes) quotes a private letter
from Holthausen making something like this suggestion,
though it had several times been thought of, though un-
published, before.

810. *Modes myrðe: Myrðe* has been taken here as an otherwise un-
recorded adj. meaning "wicked." This would be the form
of an adj. corresponding to the noun *morð.* Cf. the relation
between *word* and *wyrde,* etc. Usually *myrðe* has been
taken as a noun = "joy" (or, according to Klaeber and
others "destruction"), parallel with *fyrene* in 811.

850. *Deaðfæge deog:* MS. *deog* has been retained and translated in
accordance with Klaeber, though recent defences of this
have not been entirely convincing. The form *deȝenn* in
the *ormulum* "die", which cannot be explained from O.N.
deyja, suggests that there was an O.E. verb *deogan* "to
die" (*mori*); so that *deaþ-fæge deog* would mean
"doomed to death as he was, he died."

871. *soðe gebunded,* if rendered "correctly linked," this phrase
refers to the technique of alliteration (cf. *Sir Gawain and
the Green Knight* l. 35 "with lel letteres loken"). But
gebunden had also the sense of "adorned" (cf. 1531, 1900
etc.), and perhaps "adorned with truth" (that is historical
accuracy) might seem the more likely interpretation. Great
store was set by historical truth in such narratives, and a

direct reference to alliteration at this early date would be remarkable.

985. MS. *steda nægla gehwylc:* This difficult reading has been retained for the translation, as none of the emendations proposed (Klaeber reads *stiðra* for *steda*) seem satisfying.

987. MS. *egl* emended, with Klaeber, to *eglu.* This is plausible palaeographically, as the next word begins also with *u.*

1015. MS. *magas þara.* Though Klaeber in his revised text doubtfully retains this reading, it seems syntactically improbable. The usual emendation of *þara* to *waran* (= W.S. *wæron*) has been accepted, as formerly by Klaeber, with a semicolon after *manig.*

1068. *Finnes eaferum:* It is not necessary to insert *be,* as Klaeber has done before *Finnes:* but see his Supplem. Notes.

1071–1159. The translation follows the text of Klaeber, but differs in several points from his interpretation. The Hengest of the *lay* is assumed to have been the historical Hengest the Jute, the Half-Danes as consisting largely of mercenary Jutes in Danish (Scylding) service, and *Hengeste* of 1083 in apposition with *þeodnes ðegne* of 1085. *Forþringan* is taken to mean something like "dislodge," in view of its etymology and its use in the prose Benedictine Rule and in the *ormulum,* and the *hig* of 1085 to refer to Hengest and his men. It was, it seems likely, because Finn could not dislodge Hengest from his position (he had found some impregnable refuge), that he was willing to accept terms: and Hengest, finding himself to be able to stand an indefinite siege, may have made these strange-seeming proposals with the motive of ultimate vengeance. It is also assumed that Jutes were on either side in the feud— Hengest and his Half-Danes, and Finn a Jute (with some Jutish followers) ruling over the very closely related Frisians.

1107. *Icge gold:* The meaning of *icge* is not known, and one of the many conjectures (see ed. Chambers) has been used.

1113. *Sume on wæle crungon:* For this emphatic demonstrative use of *sum,* cf. the description of Beowulf as *eorla sum* in

1312, *The Wanderer* 80 (*sume wig fornom*), and especially l. 48 of the *Rune-poem* (where the mightily auspicious symbol for *T* is described as *tacna sum*).

1141. Klaeber now has adopted the emendation *irne* of MS. *inne* into his text, and the translation follows this.

1142. The MS. *worold rædenne* is taken as emended, with Klaeber, to w[e]orodrædende (dat. sing.), and the object (*torngemotes*) implied for *forwyrnde*. This then would be a typical O.E. meiosis.

1145. *mid eotenum:* Klaeber capitalizes *Eotenum*, making it = *Eotum* "Jutes": but unless a scribal error is assumed, it should refer rather to the *eotenas*, giants probably, among whom (as they made such magic weapons) this special sword may well have been famous. Cf. the *ealdsweord eotenisc* of 1558.

1173–1174. *geofena gemyndig . . . þū nū hafast:* "mindful (i.e. remembering to be generous) with the gifts *which* etc." Here is probably the earliest example of that omission of the relative pronoun which is a well known feature of Northern M.E. and survives in our familiar speech.

1231. MS. *doð* is here retained, as by Klaeber in his latest revision, though the emendation to *do* (imperative sing.) remains very tempting.

1260. *se þe:* "she who." Grendel's mother is referred to in the poem by both masculine and feminine pronouns, perhaps being thought of as female *qua* mother, but male *qua* demon. Like Milton's devils in *Paradise Lost,* Germanic demons seem to have been ambisexual (cf. the Gothic forms of the Biblical devils).

1320. *æfter neodlaðu[m]:* The translation follows the common interpretation accepted by Klaeber; but it might be better to take *neod* in the compound as a form of *nēd* (W.S. *nīed*) = "necessity"; and to translate the phrase as "in view of the urgency of the summons." Beowulf feared that the night had held some disaster when he found himself so pressingly summoned to the royal chamber. There is no need to insert *m* after the MS. *laðu,* which may be regarded as a dialectal dat. sing. (*laðu* = "summons").

1375. *drysmaþ:* this is clearly an error for *ðrysmaþ = þrysmað* in Classical O.E. spelling. Cf. the noun *þrosm* from which this verb has been formed. A similar confusion between *d* and *ð* appears in *Exodus* i. 40, where *þrysmyde* (late form of *þrysmode*) is written *dryrmyde* in the MS. (with also the common error of *r* for *s*). Had the verb been the regular type *þrysmian*, we should expect *þrysmiað* for the plural; but there is no need to alter the probably later form, from a later *þrysman*. The meaning of the verb is "to become dark or misty."

1382. *wundini golde:* this MS. reading is emended doubtfully to *wundnum golde* by Klaeber: but if it is accepted, it might point to a date not later than the middle of the eighth century as an early spelling, and hence be of value in tracing back the history of the written text.

1407. *ham eahtode:* this is an example of the earlier metre of O.E. requiring a secondary stress or half-lift on the *o* of *cahtode.* Cf. 1413, and especially the *ræd eahtedon* of 172 where the *e* of *eahtedon* must be emended to *o* for the sake of the metre.

1457. *hæftmece:* The exact meaning of the technical term is well discussed in Shetelig and Falk's *Scandinavian Archæology* translated by E. V. Gordon (Oxford, 1937), v. p. 379. This work is invaluable for most of the weapon-names that cause difficulty in *Beowulf.*

1487. *breac þonne mōste:* "enjoyed his bounty while I could." *Giefstōles* is to be understood after *breac:* for the phrase *giefstōles brūcan* meant "to enjoy" not the gift-seat itself, but the bounty that was distributed from it (cf. Wanderer 46).

1591. *Sona:* Schücking has made out a convincing case for taking *sona* to mean "as soon as," in the *Max Förster Festschrift* of 1929.

1724ff. *Wundor is to secganne ff:* This much-discussed homily of Hrothgar is the nearest thing to a sustained piece of Christian didacticism in the poem, and for this reason its authenticity has been questioned. It uses several motives common in the homilies of the tenth century: but stylistically it is clearly an integral part of the poem and well fitted to the almost patriarchal character of Hrothgar. Moreover it shows a perfect fusion of form and matter, and in literary quality it is one of the finest examples in *Beowulf.* The apparent allegory of Conscience "shepherd of the soul" falling asleep (1741–1742) may remind us of the early M.E. prose homily of *Sawles Warde,* composed about the end of the twelfth century. But such an idea need not necessarily mean that the passage is of late origin. The general notion of a conflict between the Christian hero and the devil embodied in that of the Germanic Beowulf and the mythological and legendary powers of darkness, seems often to underlie the poem, though never explicit.

1797–1798. *Swylce þy dōgore heaþolīðende habban scoldon:* The special retainer or chamberlain looked after "such needs as warriors on a journey used to have in those days." Here, by the expression *þy dōgore,* the poet shows his awareness of the fact that he is seeking to recall the ways of life in a past age.

1807–1809. *Heht þa se hearda . . . þæs leanes þanc:* Klaeber takes *se hearda* as Unferth, and makes him present Hrunting (which had been restored without mention by the Poet) to Beowulf as a parting gift. But, if *þæs leanes* could mean "the loan," the sense would run much more easily and involve no sudden change of subject. The translation takes this latter view, making *se hearda* Beowulf, *sunu* a dialectal dat. sing., and *leanes* = *lænes* "loan" instead of its normal sense of "gift." In late O.E. *leanes* and *lænes* would probably have been pronounced identically by a W.S. scribe; so that even if *leanes* cannot bear the meaning "loan," it may well be regarded as a natural scribal error for *lænes*.

1833. *þæt ic þē wel herige:* The translation follows Klaeber in taking *herian* to have the contextual sense of "shew esteem by deeds": but one might be tempted to assume here that *herian* is quite a different word, a homophone, derived from the noun *here* "army" and meaning "support with military power." Then the clause would mean "that I may support thee with a powerful force." This *herian* would be a unique occurrence; but such *hapax legomena* are not infrequent in our so limited remains of O.E. poetry.

1931. MS. *mod þryðo wæg:* The translation follows Klaeber's revised text, reading *Modþryðo wæg.* Objections, especially metrical, to the commonly accepted reading *mod þryðe ne wæg* are too serious. Modthrytho, or Modthryth, is assumed to be a name for Thryth (Latin. Drida), wife of Offa the Angle; and the sudden passing from Hygd to Thryth in the middle of the line (1931) may remain as the stylistic (to us moderns) abruptness of the Poet, or may be accounted for by the assumption of a missing passage introducing Thryth which has been lost between 1931*a* and 1931*b*.

2035. *duguða biwenede:* Klaeber takes *duguða* as nom. pl. in apposition with *dryhtbearn Dena* and puts a comma after *Dena:* but the translation accepts the view that *duguða* is an instrumental or adverbial gen. pl. modifying *biwenede.* Either view—and a good many others—could be defended in this difficult passage. Of course, there will be no comma after *Dena* in the translated version.

2106. *felafricgende:* This is probably an error for some word so far not recovered. The translation follows the common practice of regarding it as formed from *fela* and *gefricgan*; and the lit. rendering would be "hearing of many things" (if *fela* is a separate word) or "greatly informed" (if *fela* intensifies *fricgende* in a compound). Metre may seem rather to support the latter view: but the whole matter is one of conjecture from an erroneous text.

2183.   *Hean wæs lange:* This seems to be a folklore element in the
poem, and the youthful insignificance of Beowulf is parallel
to the sluggishness of the Danish Holger, who falls asleep
as a boy and will remain so till his country is in its direst
need, when he will spring up and become its heroic
deliverer. But the poet may possibly also be using this traditional material to mark an early stage in the hero's spiritual
development (v. Kemp Malone in *Journal of English and
Germanic Philology,* XXXVI, pp. 21ff.).

2213.   *stanbeorh steapne:* Dragons traditionally inhabited grave-
barrows where treasure had been hidden for the noble dead.

2214ff.   *þær on innan gïong* ff.: The application of ultra-violet ray
to this largely illegible portion of fol. 179 recto, has not
made it possible so far to read these half-dozen lines with
enough confidence to attempt an exact translation, though
much fascinating speculation has resulted.

2226ff.   *sona mwatide* ff.: This is unintelligible, and the next four
lines are again only partly legible. The most recent attempt
at re-examination which supplies useful new material is
that of Sedgefield in his third ed. of *Beowulf* (Manchester
Univ. Press, 1935).

2525.   *fötes trem:* This phrase, imitated in *Maldon* 247, apart from
its difficulty usually solved through the later passage, is of
interest as showing perhaps the clearest of the very rare
Kentish forms (*trem*) in the poem. We know of a school of
scribes at Canterbury, and may imagine that our text has
at some time passed through it: but this would only be
after about the later ninth century, since Kentish *e* for *y*
scarcely appears before then.

2577.   MS. *incgelafe:* The translation has adopted one of the many
guesses at the meaning of this quite obscure word.

2687.   *wæpen wundum heard:* MS. *wundum* has generally been
emended to *wundrum,* which the translation follows. But
it is perhaps conceivable that just as blood was poetically
held to harden weapons (v. 1460, where the sword
Hrunting is said to be *ahyrded heaþoswäte*) weapons may
have been "hardened by wounds" as in the MS. reading.

3005.   MS. *hwate scildingas:* The highly elaborate explanations
needed to give any meaning to this reading in the context
make its retention unsatisfying in the extreme. Klaeber's
revised edition accepts the attractive emendation of Hoops,
hwate scildwigan; and this has been adopted in the translation as being the most plausible of all so far proposed.

3074-3075.   MS. *næshe gold hwæte gearwor hæfde agendes est ær gesceawod:* This is a *locus desperatus*; but the metrical soundness of the two lines makes emendation seem unwise. Klaeber accepts the change of *næs he* to *næfne he,* putting a comma after *strude* at the end of the line above. The translation assumes a sentence ending with *strude,* and retains the MS. intact, offering a new interpretation of *goldhwæte* as an adj. = "pertaining to gold with a curse on it" qualifying the acc. fem. noun *est* "treasure." Cf. O.E. *hwatu* and *hwatung* = "augury" or "divination," *hwata* = "soothsayer," and cognates like O.S. *forhuuatan* = "curse" for this postulated sense of the element *hwæte.* For the use of *gearwor* in a superlative force, cf. 915 (*gefægra*) and *The Dream of the Rood* 4 (*syllicre treow*). The general sense seems clearly to be that Beowulf had not committed the sin of gazing avariciously on the treasure and thus did not merit the curse : by a characteristic meiosis we are told that he had not, till the last scene, gazed "too eagerly" on the owner's (the chief who had originally hidden it) treasure (*est*) of gold which had curse on it (*goldhwæte*) before ; i.e. he had never gazed on it nor desired it till then. The above conjecture is not put forward with any confidence, but merely because it has the advantage of not involving any emendation other than that of word-division, and does not seem any more improbable than the rest, while fitting the context perhaps rather better.

3150. Pope has deciphered the last half of the line (hitherto partly illegible) as *geatisc meowle,* in his *The Rhythms of Beowulf* (Yale Univ. Press, 1942), p. 233. This would settle once for all that Hygd, widow of Hygelac, had married Beowulf, and hence was the appropriate person to lead his funeral rites. The translation must then replace "aged woman" by "Geatish woman" or "woman of the Geats."

3150b–3155a. The translation follows the commonly accepted reconstruction of this partially illegible passage, as in Klaeber, except that *wraðes* is adopted (from Sedgefield's 3rd edition) for the usual *wigendes. Wigendes* has been kept by many out of respect for Zupitza (see his note to the last page of his facsimile of the MS.): but it is unsatisfactory metrically. This last leaf of the MS. (from 3150b) is faded, has holes and stains, and has suffered from partially and sometimes mistaken freshening-up by a later scribe. Cf., however, A. H. Smith on "The Photography of MSS." in *London Mediæval Studies,* I (1938), pp. 200ff., and Pope, *op. cit.,* pp. 232–233.

THE FINNESBURG FRAGMENT

The translation follows the revised text of Klaeber's third edition of *Beowulf*, where the sole authority, Hickes's version of a lost early eleventh-century MS. printed in his *Thesaurus* of 1705, will be also found.

12. *windað:* Hickes's *windað* has been retained in the translation, as Klaeber's *winnað* seems an unnecessary emendation.

34. Hickes has *Hwearflacra hrær:* Klaeber reads *hwearflicra hræw*; but this is not palaeographically likely. The translation adopts the emendation of Holthausen *hwearf blacra hræs*, slightly modified. *Blacra* is then gen. pl. of the adj. *blāc* = "pale," and *hræs* is the L.W.S. (early eleventh-century) form of *hreas*, pret. indic. of *hrēosan* "fall." *Hwearf* will thus be the noun *hwearf* = "crowd." This emendation only assumes the falling out of a *b* from *blacra* and the common confusion of *s* and *r* in *hræs*.

Verse Translation

No attempt has been made to improve the literary quality of these verses; but their sense has been generally conformed to that of the revised prose version.

GEORGE ALLEN & UNWIN LTD
London : 40 Museum Street, W.C.1

Auckland : 24 Wyndham Street
Bombay : 15 Graham Road, Ballard Estate, Bombay 1
Calcutta : 17 Chittaranjan Avenue, Calcutta 13
Cape Town : 109 Long Street
Karachi : Metherson's Estate, Wood Street, Karachi 2
New Delhi : 13-14 Ajmeri Gate Extension, New Delhi 1
São Paulo : Avenida 9 de Julho 1138-Ap. 51
Sydney, N.S.W. : Bradbury House, 55 York Street
Toronto : 91 Wellington Street West

by J. R. R. Tolkien

THE LORD OF THE RINGS

IN THREE PARTS :   *21s. net. per vol. 63s. net set*

THE FELLOWSHIP OF THE RING

THE TWO TOWERS

THE RETURN OF THE KING

' However one may look at it, *The Fellowship of the Ring* is an extraordinary book. It deals with a stupendous theme. It leads us through a succession of strange and astonishing episodes, some of them magnificent, in a region where everything is invented, forest, moor, river, wilderness, town, and the races which inhabit them.' RICHARD HUGHES in *The Observer*

THE HOBBIT

2nd Edition, 10th Impression   *Cr. 8vo 12s. 6d. net*

' One long enchantment, an ingenious story that will delight any child, crammed with episodes that will obliterate need for meals and bed.' *Times Literary Supplement*

' A glorious book . . . No normal child could resist it.'

Time and Tide

FARMER GILES OF HAM

Illustrated by Pauline Baynes   *Cr. 8vo 7s. 6d. net*

' Has that rare quality of fantasy. There is a peculiar charm in the adventures of the red-headed Giles and the wicked dragon Chrysophlax.' *Tatler*.